Project-Based Inquiry Science™

MOVING BIG THINGS

Janet L. Kolodner

Joesph S. Krajcik

Daniel C. Edelson

Brian J. Reiser

NSF

IT's ABOUT TIME®

HERFF JONES EDUCATION DIVISION

IT's ABOUT TIME®

HERFF JONES EDUCATION DIVISION

84 Business Park Drive, Armonk, NY 10504
Phone (914) 273-2233 Fax (914) 273-2227
www.its-about-time.com

President
Tom Laster

Director of Product Development
Barbara Zahm, Ph.D

Creative Director
John Nordland

Project Development Editor
Ruta Demery

Editorial Coordinator
Sarah V. Gruber

Editor/Writer
Victoria Willows

Associate Editor
Lakiska Flippin

Assistant Editor
Rhonda Gordon

Content and Safety Reviewer
Edward Robeck

Production/Studio Manager
Robert Schwalb

Layout and Production
Kadi Sarv

Production
Sean Campbell, Michael Hortens
Marie Killoran

Creative Artwork
Dennis Falcon

Technical Art
Marie Killoran
Michael Hortens

Photo Research
Carlo Cantavero

Printed and bound in the United States of America.

ISBN-13: 978-1-58591-601-6

1 2 3 4 5 VH 11 10 09 08 07

This project was supported, in part, by the **National Science Foundation**
under grant nos. 0137807, 0527341, 0639978.
Opinions expressed are those of the authors and not necessarily
those of the National Science Foundation.

PBIS Principal Investigators

Janet L. Kolodner is a Regents' Professor in the School of Interactive Computing in Georgia Institute of Technology's College of Computing. Since 1978, her research has focused on learning from experience, both in computers and in people. She pioneered the Artificial Intelligence method called *case-based reasoning*, providing a way for computers to solve new problems based on their past experiences. Her book, *Case-Based Reasoning*, synthesizes work across the case-based reasoning research community from its inception to 1993.

Since 1994, Dr. Kolodner has focused on the applications and implications of case-based reasoning for education. In her approach to science education, called Learning by Design™ (LBD), students learn science while pursuing design challenges. Dr. Kolodner has investigated how to create a culture of collaboration and rigorous science talk in classrooms, how to use a project challenge to promote focus on science content, and how students learn and develop when classrooms function as learning communities. Currently, Dr. Kolodner is investigating how to help young people come to think of themselves as scientific reasoners. Dr. Kolodner's research results have been widely published, including in *Cognitive Science, Design Studies,* and the *Journal of the Learning Sciences.*

Dr. Kolodner was founding Director of Georgia Techs' EduTech Institute, served as coordinator of Georgia Techs' Cognitive Science program for many years, and is founding Editor in Chief of the *Journal of the Learning Sciences.* She is a founder of the International Society for the Learning Sciences (ISLS), and she served as its first Executive Officer. She is a fellow of the American Association of Artificial Intelligence (AAAI).

Joseph S. Krajcik is a Professor of Science Education and Associate Dean for Research in the School of Education at the University of Michigan. He works with teachers in science classrooms to bring about sustained change by creating classroom environments in which students find solutions to important intellectual questions that subsume essential curriculum standards and use learning technologies as productivity tools. He seeks to discover what students learn in such environments, as well as to explore and find solutions to challenges that teachers face in enacting such complex instruction. Professor Krajcik has authored and co-authored over 100 manuscripts and makes frequent presentations at international, national and regional conferences that focus on his research, as well as presentations that translate research findings into classroom practice. He is a fellow of the American Association for the Advancement of Science and served as president of the National Association for Research in Science Teaching. Dr. Krajcik co-directs the Center for Highly Interactive Classrooms, Curriculum and Computing in Education at the University of Michigan and is a co-principal investigator in the Center for Curriculum Materials in Science and The National Center for Learning and Teaching Nanoscale Science and Engineering. In 2002, Professor Krajcik was honored to receive a Guest Professorship from Beijing Normal University in Beijing, China. In winter 2005, he was the Weston Visiting Professor of Science Education at the Weizmann Institute of Science in Rehovot, Israel.

Daniel C. Edelson is director of the Geographic Data in Education (GEODE) Initiative at Northwestern University where he is an Associate Professor of the Learning Sciences and Computer Science. Trained as a computer and cognitive scientist, Dr. Edelson develops and studies software and curricula that are informed by contemporary research on learning and motivation. Since 1992, Dr. Edelson has directed a series of projects exploring the use of technology as a catalyst for reform in science education and has led the development of a number of software environments for education. These include My World GIS, a geographic information system for inquiry-based learning, and WorldWatcher, a data visualization and analysis system for gridded geographic data, both of which have been recognized by educators for their contributions to Earth science education. Dr. Edelson is the author of the high school environmental science text, *Investigations in Environmental Science: A Case-Based Approach to the Study of Environmental Systems*. Dr. Edelson is currently engaged in research on professional development and implementation support for schools that have adopted *Investigations in Environmental Science*.

Since 1995, he has been the principal investigator on more than a dozen NSF-funded educational research and development grants, and he is a member of the leadership team of the NSF-funded Center for Curriculum Materials in Science. His research has been widely published, including in the *Journal of the Learning Sciences,* the *Journal of Research on Science Teaching,* the *Journal of Geoscience Education*, and *Science Teacher*.

Brian J. Reiser is a Professor of Learning Sciences in the School of Education and Social Policy at Northwestern University. Professor Reiser served as chair of Northwestern's Learning Sciences Ph.D. program from 1993, shortly after its inception, until 2001. His research focuses on the design and enactment of learning environments that support students' inquiry in science, including both science curriculum materials and scaffolded software tools. His research investigates the design of learning environments that scaffold scientific practices, including investigation, argumentation, and explanation; design principles for technology-infused curricula that engage students in inquiry projects; and the teaching practices that support student inquiry.

Professor Reiser also directed BGuILE (Biology Guided Inquiry Learning Environments) to develop software tools for supporting middle school and high school students in analyzing data and constructing explanations with biological data. Reiser is a co-principal investigator in the NSF Center for Curriculum Materials in Science. He recently served as a member of the NRC panel authoring the report *Taking Science to School*. Professor Reiser received his Ph.D. in Cognitive Science from Yale University in 1983.

Acknowledgements

Three research teams contributed to the development of Project-Based Inquiry Science (PBIS): a team at Georgia Institute of Technology headed by Janet L. Kolodner, a team at Northwestern University headed by Daniel Edelson and Brian Reiser, and a team at University of Michigan headed by Joseph Krajcik and Ron Marx. Each of the PBIS units was originally developed by one of these teams and then later revised and edited to be a part of the full three-year middle-school curriculum that became PBIS.

PBIS has its roots in two educational approaches, Project-Based Science and Learning by Design™. Project-Based Science suggests that students should learn science through engaging in the same kinds of inquiry practices scientists use, in the context of scientific problems relevant to their lives and using tools authentic to science. Project-Based Science was originally conceived in the hi-ce Center at University of Michigan, with funding from the National Science Foundation. Learning by Design™ derives from Problem-Based Learning and suggests sequencing, social practices, and reflective activities for promoting learning. It engages students in design practices, including the use of iteration and deliberate reflection. LBD was conceived at Georgia Institute of Technology, with funding from the National Science Foundation, DARPA, and the McDonnell Foundation.

The development of the integrated PBIS curriculum was supported by the National Science Foundation under grants nos. 0137807, 0527341, and 0639978. Any opinions, findings and conclusions, or recommendations expressed in this material are those of the authors and do not necessarily reflect the views of the National Science Foundation.

PBIS Team

Principal Investigator
Janet L. Kolodner

Co-Principal Investigators
Daniel C. Edelson
Joseph S. Krajcik
Brian J. Reiser

NSF Program Officer
Gerhard Salinger

Curriculum Developers
Michael T. Ryan
Mary L. Starr

Teacher's Edition Developers
Rebecca M. Schneider
Mary L. Starr

Literacy Specialist
LeeAnn M. Sutherland

NSF Program Reviewer
Arthur Eisenkraft

Project Coordinator
Juliana Lancaster

External Evaluators
The Learning Partnership
Steven M. McGee
Jennifer Witers

The Georgia Institute of Technology Team

Project Director:
Janet L. Kolodner

Development of PBIS units at the Georgia Institute of Technology was conducted in conjunction with the Learning by Design™ Research group (LBD), Janet L. Kolodner, PI.

Lead Developers, Physical Science:
David Crismond
Michael T. Ryan

Lead Developer, Earth Science:
Paul J. Camp

Assessment and Evaluation:
Barbara Fasse
Daniel Hickey
Jackie Gray
Laura Vandewiele
Jennifer Holbrook

Project Pioneers:
JoAnne Collins
David Crismond
Joanna Fox
Alice Gertzman
Mark Guzdial
Cindy Hmelo-Silver
Douglas Holton
Roland Hubscher
N. Hari Narayanan
Wendy Newstetter
Valery Petrushin
Kathy Politis
Sadhana Puntambekar
David Rector
Janice Young

The Northwestern University Team

Project Directors:
Daniel Edelson
Brian Reiser

Lead Developer, Biology:
David Kanter

Lead Developers, Earth Science:
Jennifer Mundt Leimberer
Darlene Slusher

Development of PBIS units at Northwestern was conducted in conjunction with:

The Center for Learning Technologies in Urban Schools (LeTUS) at Northwestern, and the Chicago Public Schools
Louis Gomez, PI;
Clifton Burgess, PI
for Chicago Public Schools.

The BioQ Collaborative
David Kanter, PI.

The Biology Guided Learning Environments (BGuILE) Project
Brian Reiser, PI.

The Geographic Data in Education (GEODE) Initiative
Daniel Edelson, Director

The Center for Curriculum Materials in Science at Northwestern
Brian Reiser,
Daniel Edelson,
Bruce Sherin, PIs.

The University of Michigan Team

Project Directors:
Joseph Krajcik
Ron Marx

Literacy Specialist:
LeeAnn M. Sutherland

Project Coordinator:
Mary L. Starr

Development of PBIS units at University of Michigan was conducted in conjunction with:

The Center for Learning Technologies in Urban Schools (LeTUS)
Ron Marx, Phyllis Blumenfeld,
Barry Fishman,
Joseph Krajcik,
Elliot Soloway, PIs.

The Detroit Public Schools
Juanita Clay-Chambers
Deborah Peek-Brown

The Center for Highly Interactive Computing in Education (hi-ce)
Ron Marx,
Phyllis Blumenfeld,
Barry Fishman,
Joe Krajcik,
Elliot Soloway,
Elizabeth Moje,
LeeAnn Sutherland, PIs.

Field-Test Teachers

National Field Test
Tamica Andrew
Leslie Baker
Jeanne Bayer
Gretchen Bryant
Boris Consuegra
Daun D'Aversa
Candi DiMauro
Kristie L. Divinski
Donna M. Dowd
Jason Fiorito
Lara Fish
Christine Gleason
Christine Hallerman
Terri L. Hart-Parker
Jennifer Hunn
Rhonda K. Hunter
Jessica Jones
Dawn Kuppersmith
Anthony F. Lawrence
Ann Novak
Rise Orsini
Tracy E. Parham
Cheryl Sgro-Ellis
Debra Tenenbaum
Sara B. Topper
Becky Watts
Debra A. Williams
Ingrid M. Woolfolk
Ping-Jade Yang

New York City Field Test
Several sequences of PBIS units have been field tested in New York City under the leadership of Whitney Lukens, Staff Developer for Region 9, and Greg Borman, Science Instructional Specialist, New York City Department of Education

6th Grade
Norman Agard
Tazinmudin Ali
Heather Guthartz
Aniba
Asher Arzonane
Asli Aydin

Joshua Blum
Filomena Borrero
Shareese Blakely
John J. Blaylock
Tsedey Bogale
Zachary Brachio
Thelma Brown
Alicia Browne-Jones
Scott Bullis
Maximo Cabral
Lionel Callender
Matthew Carpenter
Ana Maria Castro
Diane Castro
Anne Chan
Ligia Chiorean
Boris Consuegra
Careen Halton Cooper
Cinnamon Czarnecki
Kristin Decker
Nancy Dejean
Gina DiCicco
Donna Dowd
Lizanne Espina
Joan Ferrato
Matt Finnerty
Jacqueline Flicker
Helen Fludd
Leigh Summers Frey
Helene Friedman-Hager
Diana Gering
Matthew Giles
Lucy Gill
Steven Gladden
Greg Grambo
Carrie Grodin-Vehling
Stephan Joanides
Kathryn Kadei
Paraskevi Karangunis
Cynthia Kerns
Martine Lalanne
Erin Lalor
Jennifer Lerman
Sara Lugert
Whitney Lukens
Dana Martorella
Christine Mazurek
Janine McGeown
Chevelle McKeever
Kevin Meyer
Jennifer Miller

Nicholas Miller
Diana Neligan
Caitlin Van Ness
Marlyn Orque
Eloisa Gelo Ortiz
Gina Papadopoulos
Tim Perez
Albertha Petrochilos
Christopher Poli
Kristina Rodriguez
Nadiesta Sanchez
Annette Schavez
Hilary Sedgwitch
Elissa Seto
Laura Shectman
Audrey Shmuel
Katherine Silva
Ragini Singhal
C. Nicole Smith
Gitangali Sohit
Justin Stein
Thomas Tapia
Eilish Walsh-Lennon
Lisa Wong
Brian Yanek
Cesar Yarleque
David Zaretsky
Colleen Zarinsky

7th Grade
Mayra Amaro
Emmanuel Anastasiou
Cheryl Barnhill
Bryce Cahn
Ligia Chiorean
Ben Colella
Boris Consuegra
Careen Halton Cooper
Elizabeth Derse
Urmilla Dhanraj
Gina DiCicco
Lydia Doubleday
Lizanne Espina
Matt Finnerty
Steven Gladden
Stephanie Goldberg
Nicholas Graham
Robert Hunter
Charlene Joseph
Ketlynne Joseph
Kimberly Kavazanjian

Christine Kennedy
Bakwah Kotung
Lisa Kraker
Anthony Lett
Herb Lippe
Jennifer Lopez
Jill Mastromarino
Kerry McKie
Christie Morgado
Patrick O'Connor
Agnes Ochiagha
Tim Perez
Nadia Piltser
Chris Poli
Carmelo Ruiz
Kim Sanders
Leslie Schiavone
Ileana Solla
Jacqueline Taylor
Purvi Vora
Ester Wiltz
Carla Yuille
Marcy Sexauer Zacchea
Lidan Zhou

Moving Big Things

Moving Big Things is adapted from two previous Units: *Building Big Things*, developed at University of Michigan, and *Machines that Help*, developed at Georgia Institute of Technology. *Building Big Things* was developed as part of the work of the Center for Learning Technologies in Urban Schools and as a project of University of Michigan's Center for Highly Interactive Computing in Education. *Machines that Help* was developed as part of the Learning by Design ™ initiative. *Moving Big Things* was developed by the Project-Based Inquiry Science team in conjunction with development teams at the University of Michigan and Georgia Institute of Technology.

Moving Big Things

PBIS Development Team
Michael T. Ryan
Mary L. Starr

Contributing field-test teachers
Asher Arzonane
Matthew Carpenter
Anne Chan
Lizanne Espina
Enrique Garcia
Steven Gladden
Dani Horowitz
Stephan Joanides
Sunny Kam
Crystal Marsh
Tim Perez
Christopher Poli
Nadiesta Sanchez
Caitlin Van Ness
Cesar Yarleque
Renee Zalewitz

Building Big Things

Project Director:
Joseph S. Krajcik

Lead Developer:
Ann E. Rivet

Other Developers:
Robert Giere

Reviewer:
Uri Ganiel

Pilot teachers and contributing developers:
Deborah Piik-Brown
Mary Joe Tarrien
Deborah LeClerc
Karen Amati
Kathleen Pett

Machines That Help

Project Director:
Janet L. Kolodner

Developers:
David Crismond
Michael T. Ryan

Graphics Design:
David Crismond

Pilot teachers:
Rudo Kashiri
Tonia Laman
Carol Pennington
Cindy Rhew
Mike Ryan
Leslie Baker

The development of *Moving Big Things* was supported by the National Science Foundation under grants no. 0137807, 0527341, and 0639978. The development of *Building Big Things* was supported by the National Science Foundation under grants no. 0803 310 A632 354. The development of *Machines that Help* was supported by the National Science Foundation under grants no. 9553585 and 9818828. Any opinions, findings, and conclusions or recommendations expressed in this material are those of the authors and do not necessarily reflect the views of the National Science Foundation.

Table of Contents

Introducing PBIS

What Do Scientists Do?

1) Scientists...address big challenges and big questions.

You will find many different kinds of big challenges and questions in PBIS units. Some ask you to think about why something is a certain way. Some ask you to think about what causes something to change. Some challenge you to design a solution to a problem. Most of them are about things that can and do happen in the real world.

Understand the Big Challenge or Question

As you get started with each Unit, you will do activities that help you understand the *Big Question* or *Challenge* for that Unit. You will think about what you already know that might help you, and you will identify some of the new things you will need to learn.

Project Board

The *Project Board* helps you keep track of your learning. For each challenge or question, you will use a *Project Board* to keep track of what you know, what you need to learn, and what you are learning. As you learn and gather evidence, you will record that on the *Project Board*. After you have answered each small question or challenge, you will return to the *Project Board* to record how what you've learned helps you answer the *Big Question* or *Challenge*.

Learning Sets

Each Unit is composed of a group of *Learning Sets*, one for each of the smaller questions that needs to be answered to address the big question or challenge. In each *Learning Set*, you will investigate and read to find answers to the *Learning Set's* question. You will also have a chance to share the results of your investigations with your classmates and work together to make sense of what you are learning. As you come to understand answers to the questions on the *Project Board*, you will record those answers and the evidence you've collected that convinces you of what you've learned. At the end of each *Learning Set*, you will apply what you've learned to the big question or challenge.

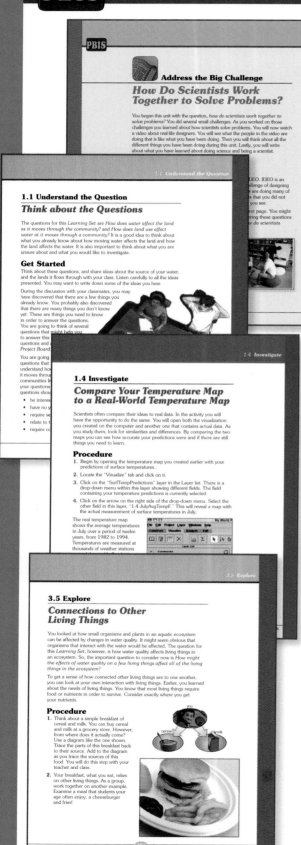

Address the Big Challenge/ Answer the Big Question

At the end of each *Unit*, you will put everything you have learned together to tackle the *Big Challenge* or *Question*.

2) Scientists...address smaller questions and challenges.

What You Do in a Learning Set

Understanding the Question or Challenge

At the start of each *Learning Set*, you will usually do activities that will help you understand the *Learning Set's* question or challenge and recognize what you already know that can help you answer the question or achieve the challenge. Usually, you will visit the *Project Board* after these activities and record on it the even smaller questions that you need to investigate to answer a *Learning Set's* question.

Investigate/Explore

There are many different kinds of investigations you might do to find answers to questions. In the *Learning Sets* you might

- Design and run experiments
- Design and run simulations
- Design and build models
- Examine large sets of data

Don't worry if you haven't done these things before. The text will provide you with lots of help in designing your investigations and in analyzing your data.

Read

Like scientists, you will also read about the science you are learning. You'll read a little bit before you investigate, but most of the reading you do will be to help you understand what you've experienced or seen in an investigation. Each time you read, the text will include *Stop and Think* questions after the reading. These questions will help you gauge how well you understand what you have read. Usually, the class will discuss the answers to *Stop and Think* questions before going on so that everybody has a chance to make sense of the reading.

Design and Build

When the *Big Challenge* for a Unit asks you to design something, the challenge in a *Learning Set* might also ask you to design something and make it work. Often you will design a part of the thing you will design and build for the big challenge. When a *Learning Set* challenges you to design and build something, you will do several things:

- Identify what questions you need to answer to be successful

- Investigate to find answers to those questions

- Use those answers to plan a good design solution

- Build and test your design

Because designs don't always work the way you want them to, you will usually do a design challenge more than once. Each time through, you will test your design. If your design doesn't work as well as you'd like, you will determine why it is not working and identify other things you need to learn to make it work better. Then you will learn those things and try again.

Explain and Recommend

A big part of what scientists do is explain, or try to make sense of why things happen the way they do. An explanation describes why something is the way it is or behaves the way it does. An explanation is a statement you make built from claims (what you think you know), evidence (from an investigation) that supports the claim, and science knowledge. As they learn, scientists get better at explaining. You'll see that you get better too as you work through the *Learning Sets*.

A recommendation is a special kind of claim—one where you advise somebody about what to do. You will make recommendations and support them with evidence, science knowledge, and explanations.

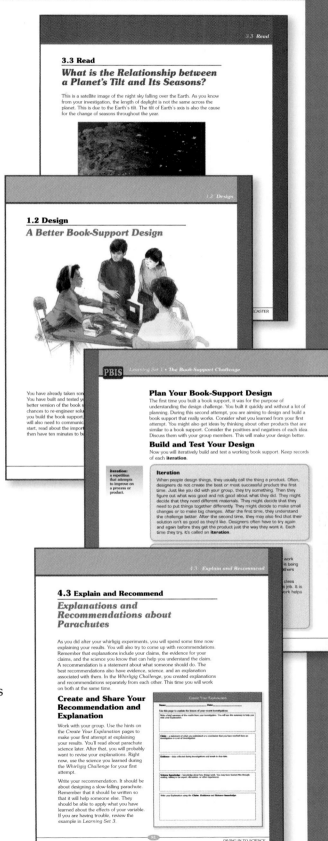

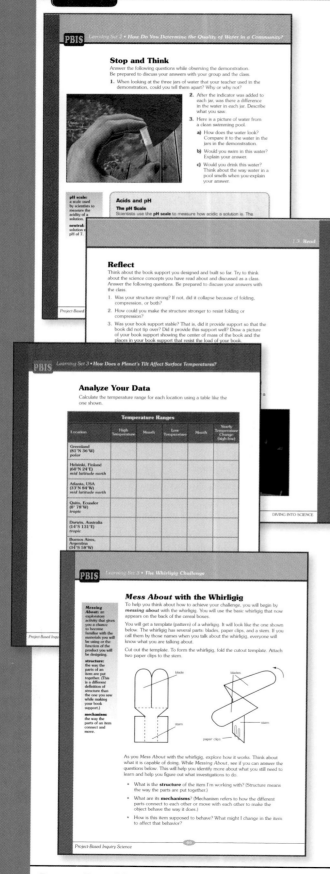

3) Scientists...reflect in many different ways.

PBIS provides guidance to help you think about what you are doing and to recognize what you are learning. Doing this often as you are working will help you be a successful student scientist.

Tools for Making Sense

Stop and Think

Stop and Think sections help you make sense of what you've been doing in the section you are working on. *Stop and Think* sections include a set of questions to help you understand what you've just read or done. Sometimes the questions will remind you of something you need to pay more attention to. Sometimes they will help you connect what you've just read to things you already know. When there is a *Stop and Think* in the text, you will work individually or with a partner to answer the questions, and then the whole class will discuss what you've learned.

Reflect

Reflect sections help you connect what you've just done with other things you've read or done earlier in the Unit (or in another unit). When there is a *Reflect* in the text, you will work individually or with a partner or your small group to answer the questions, and then the whole class will discuss what you've learned. You may be asked to answer *Reflect* questions for homework.

Analyze Your Data

Whenever you have to analyze data, the text will provide hints about how to do that and what to look for.

Mess About

"Messing about" is a term that comes from design. It means exploring the materials you will be using for designing or building something or examining something that works like what you will be designing. Messing about helps you discover new ideas—and it can be a lot of fun. The text will usually give you ideas about things to notice as you are messing about.

What's the Point?

At the end of each *Learning Set*, you will find a summary, called *What's the Point*, of the important things we hope you learned from the *Learning Set*. These summaries can help you remember how what you did and learned is connected to the big challenge or question you are working on.

4) Scientists...collaborate.

Scientists never do all their work alone. They work with other scientists (collaborate) and share their knowledge. PBIS helps you be a student scientist by giving you lots of opportunities for sharing your findings, ideas, and discoveries with others (the way scientists do). You will work together in small groups to investigate, design, explain, and do other things. Sometimes you will work in pairs to figure things out together. You will also have lots of opportunities to share your findings with the rest of your classmates and make sense together of what you are learning.

Investigation Expo

In an *Investigation Expo*, small groups report to the class about an investigation they've done. For each *Investigation Expo*, you will make a poster detailing what you were trying to learn from your investigation, what you did, your data, and your interpretation of your data. The text gives you hints about what to present and what to look for in other groups' presentations. *Investigation Expos* are always followed by discussions about what you've learned and about how to do science well. You may also be asked to write a lab report following an investigation.

Plan Briefing/Solution Briefing/Idea Briefing

Briefings are presentations of work in progress. They give you a chance to get advice from your classmates that can help you move forward. During a *Plan Briefing*, you present your plan to the class. It might be a plan for an experiment or a plan for solving a problem or achieving a challenge. During a *Solution Briefing*, you present your solution in progress and ask the class to help you make your solution better. During an *Idea Briefing*, you present your ideas. You get the best advice from your classmates when you present evidence in support of your plan, solution, or idea. Often, you will prepare a poster to help you make your presentation. Briefings are almost always followed by discussions of what you've learned and how you will move forward.

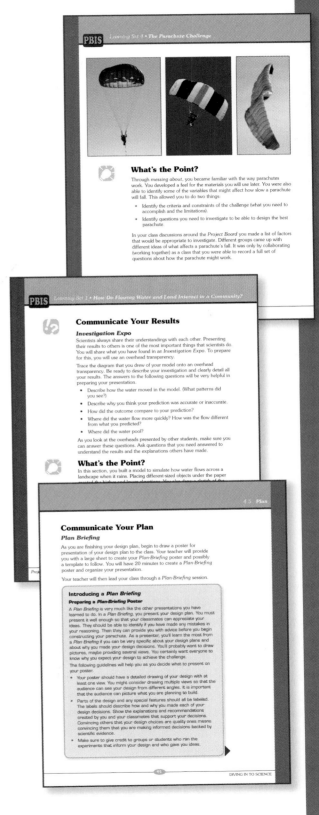

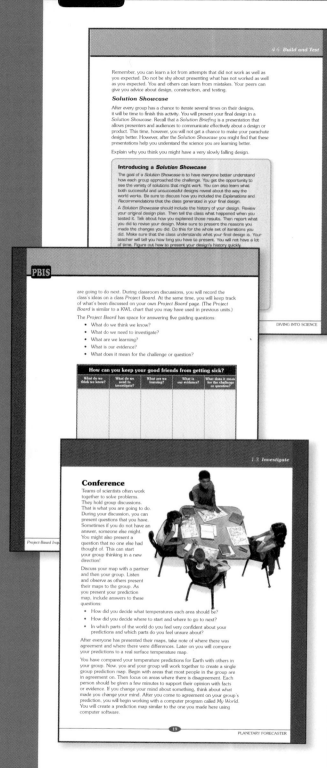

Solution Showcase

Solution Showcases usually appear near the end of a Unit. During a *Solution Showcases*, you show your classmates your finished product—either your answer to a question or your solution to a challenge. You also tell the class why you think it is a good answer or solution, what evidence and science you used to get to your solution, and what you tried along the way before getting to your answer or solution. Sometimes a *Solution Showcases* is followed by a competition. It is almost always followed by a discussion comparing and contrasting the different answers and solutions groups have come up with. You may be asked to write a report or paper following a *Solution Showcases*.

Update the *Project Board*

Remember that the *Project Board* is designed to help the class keep track of what they are learning and their progress towards a Unit's *Big Question* or *Big Challenge*. At the beginning of each Unit, the class creates a *Project Board*, and together you record what you think you know about answering the big question or addressing the *Big Challenge* and what you think you need to investigate further. Near the beginning of each *Learning Set*, the class revisits the *Project Board* and adds new questions and things they think they know to the *Project Board*. At the end of each *Learning Set*, the class again revisits the *Project Board*. This time you record what you have learned, the evidence you've collected, and recommendations you can make about answering the *Big Question* or achieving the *Big Challenge*.

Conference

A *Conference* is a short discussion between a small group of students before a more formal whole-class discussion. Students might discuss predictions and observations, they might try to explain together, they might consult on what they think they know, and so on. Usually a *Conference* is followed by a discussion around the *Project Board*. In these small group discussions, everybody gets a chance to participate.

What's the Point?
Review what you have learned in each *Learning Set*.

Communicate
Share your ideas and results with your classmates.

Stop and Think
Answer questions that help you understand what you've done in a section.

Record
Record your data as you gather it.

Project-Based Inquiry Science

What's the Big Question?

How do machines help move large, heavy objects?

When you think of heavy objects, you might think of a box of books, a large appliance, a car, or mounds of dirt and rock. There are plenty of heavy things in the world that need to be moved. Sometimes people can use their own strength to move something heavy. At other times, the object is so heavy that even the strongest person cannot move it. This is when a machine must be used. A machine is anything that helps you do work or makes work easier.

There are many kinds of machines that people use to move things. Some of them are big machines like tractors and bulldozers. You may have seen examples of these machines at construction sites in your area. There are also smaller machines that are handheld. You may have used some of these at home. A hammer, a saw, and a screwdriver are examples of small machines.

In this Unit, you are going to investigate how the movement of an object is related to forces pushing or pulling on it. You will learn how different types of machines can increase the force you apply to an object. You and your class will use what you are learning to solve a problem of moving a large, heavy crate to the top of a 20 m (65 ft) cliff. You will give advice about the kinds of equipment required to do this. You will read more about this challenge on the next page.

Look at the *Big Question* for this Unit: *How do machines help move large, heavy objects?* This is a very big question. To answer it, you will need to break it down into smaller questions that you can answer. You probably already have some smaller questions that you might want to ask. You may also have ideas that you would like to discuss with the class. You will have a chance to ask those questions and discuss your ideas when you start working on your class *Project Board*. As you move through this Unit, you will answer several smaller questions to help you answer the *Big Question*.

Welcome to Moving Big Things.
This is a great opportunity for you to work as
a student scientist.

Get Started

You are going to learn about some of the machines that make big buildings, homes, bridges, roads, and much more possible. Your teacher will arrange for you to visit a construction site either by actually going to one or by watching a video of one.

As you explore the construction site, identify the machines being used, the materials on the site, and the kinds of tasks being done. Record any questions or ideas you might have about machines. Use the diagram to help you identify some of the machines that you see.

Record your observations. Also, draw pictures of any equipment or materials that are not shown in the diagram or that you cannot identify.

Stop and Think

1. What types of objects were machines moving?

2. What machines were being used? How did each machine move big objects? Did the machine lift and carry the object or push it along the ground?

3. What was on the site before the construction?

4. Describe the area around the building (trees, rocks, concrete). How were machines being used to move any of these objects?

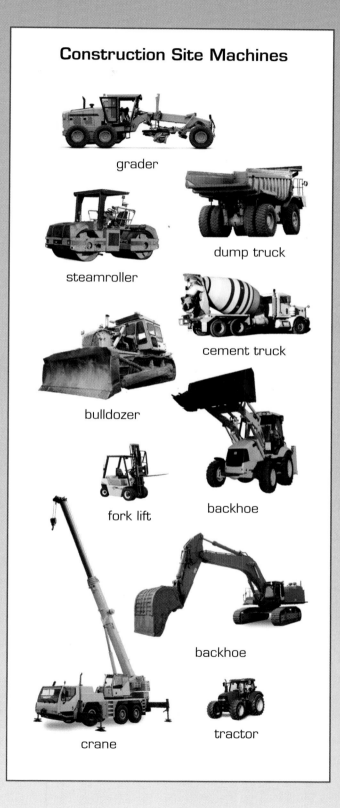

Construction Site Machines

grader

steamroller

dump truck

cement truck

bulldozer

fork lift

backhoe

backhoe

crane

tractor

5. What kinds of tasks did you see the workers doing *without* machines?

6. Describe any other observations, related to building or machines, that you thought were interesting.

Think about the *Big Question*

In this Unit, you will need to respond to a challenge to answer the *Big Question*. Before you start to think about what you already know about the *Big Question*, read about the challenge you will need to address.

Your Challenge

In the middle of the Pacific Ocean is an island that has never been inhabited by humans. The next closest island is 130 km (81 mi) away. The island is the site of a 1965 shipwreck. The ship is still grounded on the island's sandy beach.

Recently a group of historians decided to visit the site and explore the cargo ship and its contents. They were hoping to find clues that would tell them more about the accident. As they were photographing the shipwreck, one of the historians took a picture of a bird perched on the front of the ship. The bird in the picture turned out to be very rare. In fact, it was a kind of bird that was thought to be extinct. When a group of biologists heard about the photo, they were very excited to know this species had survived.

model:
a way of representing something in the world to learn more about it.

Three biologists, Drs. Enrique Cortez, Susan Diamond, and Tanika Patankar, will be traveling to the island to begin a yearlong study of the bird. They will set up a campsite on a cliff. The top of the cliff is 20 m (65 ft) above the beach and water. Since the island is surrounded by salty ocean water, they will need freshwater, food, and other supplies. Once a month, these supplies will be dropped from an airplane. Using a parachute, the supplies will be dropped in a large crate about the size of a car. The safest place to make the drop is on the beach.

The food, freshwater, and other supplies are very important for the team's survival. They will need to get the items in the crate from the beach up to the top of the cliff. One way to do that would be to empty the crate and carry the supplies up one item at a time. But, if they can get the crate itself up the cliff, they will be able to use it as a source of firewood. The team is looking for a way to get the crate from the beach to the top of the cliff.

The crate is very heavy. The scientists will not be able to lift it together or carry it up the cliff. They also will not have any equipment or motorized devices, such as a tractor or truck, to help them move the crate. They will bring some tools to the island. There are also materials from the beached cargo ship that might prove helpful. Your class is going to help out by investigating possible solutions for them to use.

Since you cannot actually join the scientists on the island, you will need to create a **model** of the solution. Your teacher has a box that is a scaled-down model of the cliff. (Scaled-down means smaller than the actual size.) There is a pole rising out of the box. It represents a large palm tree that is at the top of the cliff, near the scientists' campsite. It may be useful in your solution to the problem. There is also a weight with the box. It represents the crate.

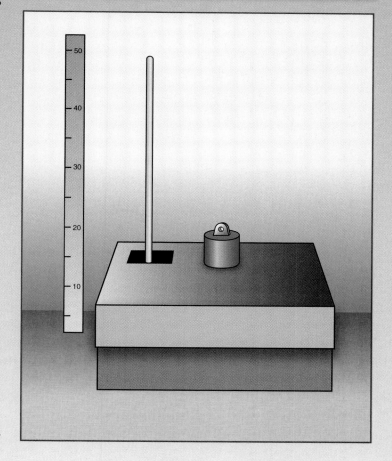

Your task is to figure out how to lift the weight (the crate) to the top of the box (the cliff) using a machine. The design of your machine will do two things. It will serve as a recommendation to the scientists for what they could build to lift the crate. Your design will also help you answer the *Big Question*: *How do machines help move large, heavy objects?*

Mess About

Drs. Enrique, Susan, and Tanika know that there is a room full of 100 m (328 ft) ropes on the wrecked cargo ship. These ropes can be used to help get the crate to the top of the cliff. By definition, a machine can be as simple as a single rope. You can begin by starting with the simplest solution and testing to see if it will work. In this case, you will see if the weight can be lifted using only the rope. However, the rope is old. It has weakened over years of exposure to the saltwater air. Therefore, you will model it with a single strand of cotton thread.

You will be using **only** the rope. Therefore, the "crate" will have to be lifted straight up from the ground. Weightlifters do something called the dead lift. The rules of dead lifting are simple. You must raise a barbell straight off the floor, up to your knees, until your legs and back are straight. To model the relative strength of the rope you will use one single strand of thread. You will loop and attach the thread to the weight to see if the thread (rope) is strong enough to lift the weight (crate) directly. You will "dead lift" a weight using a single strand of thread.

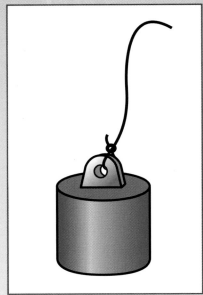

1. Prepare the weight for the dead lift. Before you lift the weight with the thread, you must attach the thread to the weight. To attach the thread, follow these steps:

- Tie a knot with a small loop at one end of the thread (the loop should be about the size of a dime).

- Wrap the cord around the hook on the weight and pass the free end of the cord through the loop. This will make a lasso that is fitted around the hook.

- Tighten the lasso around the weight's hook by hand.

2. Get a model of the cliff from your teacher. You will be using this model throughout the Unit.

3. Attach a single thread to the weight. Try to lift the weight straight up to the top of the box. Record your results in a data table similar to the one shown.

Number of strands of thread	Able to lift weight? (yes or no)
1	
2	
3	
4	
5	
6	
7	
8	

4. One by one, attach additional loops to the hook on the weight. Hold all the loops attached to the weight. Try to lift it to the top of the box without the threads breaking. Continue to record your results in the data table.

Helpful hint: Tie each strand to the hook separately. Do not double the thread or make a U-shape through the loop. This will give inaccurate results. One way would be to start with seven or eight prepared loops. Then, add these prepared loops one by one.

5. Determine the number of thread loops it requires to lift the weight to the top of the box.

Communicate

Once every group has completed the activity, your teacher will bring the class together. Be prepared to discuss the results of your activity with the class. Consider how the results will affect your possible solution.

Criteria and Constraints

You found that a single thread is too weak. This means that a single rope will be too weak to directly lift the crate up the cliff. That is why a machine is going to be necessary to get the task done. You will need to design a machine so Drs. Enrique, Susan, and Tanika can move the crate up the cliff without breaking the rope.

You now have a set of requirements to guide the design of your machine. The chart shows how these requirements compare to the real requirements for the machine needed on the island.

criteria: goals that must be satisfied to be able to successfully acheive a challenge.

constraints: factors that limit how you can solve a problem.

Biologists' machine	Your model machine
1. Must lift a *crate of supplies*.	1. Must lift a *weight*.
2. Must lift the crate about *20 m* to the top of the cliff.	2. Must lift the weight about *20 cm* to the top of the box.
3. Biologists have a *weak rope* and other materials found on the island.	3. Must use a *single strand of thread* and the materials and equipment supplied by the teacher.

If it took three strands of thread to lift the weight, the machine you build must supply a *pull* three times larger than the rope can handle. How many strands of thread did you need to lift the weight? Use this information to fill in the second column of the table. Look back at the table you created.

With your class, identify the **criteria** and **constraints** for this challenge. Use requirements listed in the table. Also, identify and record any criteria and constraints that may not appear in the table, but that you think are important or necessary.

Create a *Project Board*

It is useful, when you are working on a design project or trying to answer a hard question or solve a hard problem, to keep track of your progress. You also want to keep track of what you still need to do. Throughout this Unit, you will be using a *Project Board* to do that. During classroom discussions, your teacher or a student will record the class's ideas on a class *Project Board*. At the same time, you will keep track of what has been discussed on your own *Project Board* page.

Recall that a *Project Board* has space for answering five guiding questions.

- What do we think we know?
- What do we need to investigate?
- What are we learning?
- What is our evidence?
- What does it mean for the challenge or question?

To get started on this *Project Board*, you need to identify and record the important science question you need to answer: *How do machines help move large, heavy objects?*. You will also record your challenge: *How can the scientists lift the crate to the top of the cliff?*

What do we think we know?

In this column of the *Project Board*, you will record what you think you know about machines that help to move, lift, and carry large, heavy objects. Discuss and post the things you think you and your classmates know about machines and forces. Have you studied these concepts before? What did you learn then? Even if it is a small fact or idea, talk about it. Discuss any factors that you might think affect moving large, heavy objects.

What do we need to investigate?

In this column, you will record the things you think you need to investigate to answer the question and achieve the challenge. During your group and class discussions, you may have found that others in your group disagreed with some of your ideas. You may not know how machines work or how they can help in this situation. This second column is designed to help you keep track of things that are debatable, unknown, and need to be investigated.

Later in this Unit, you will return to the *Project Board*. For now, work with your classmates and follow your teacher's instructions as you begin filling in its first two columns.

Learning Set 1

What Makes Things Move?

The scientists on the island have a problem. They must *move* a heavy crate up to the top of the cliff. It is probably obvious to you at this point that machines can help move things. However, you may not know how they do this. Before you can begin to understand how machines move things, you need to understand why things move. What causes something to move from one location to another?

To answer the *Big Question*, you need to break it down into smaller questions. In this *Learning Set,* you are going to answer the question *What makes things move?*. Answering this question is the first step toward achieving the challenge and answering the *Big Question*: *How do machines help move large, heavy objects?*.

What enables you to lift a backpack and carry it forward?

1.1 Understand the Question

Thinking about What Makes Things Move

The question for this *Learning Set* is *What makes things move?*. You see things move all the time. Soccer balls get kicked, papers get shuffled, leaves get blown, and chairs get pushed. To answer the question about what makes things move, it is a good idea to think about what you already know about making things move. It is also important to think about what you do not know or are unsure about.

You will observe a class demonstration about pushing, pulling, and moving a heavy bucket. Then you will begin to learn more about how and why objects can move.

Demonstration

Your teacher will demonstrate three different pushes and pulls on a heavy bucket. Your teacher will repeat the demonstration three times. Each time the push and pull on the bucket will be greater. Observe how the bucket's motion changes with each push and pull. Record your observations.

Conference

force: a push or a pull resulting from an object's interaction with another object.

So far, you have been talking about pushes and pulls. Your teacher pushed and pulled the bucket, the machines at the construction site pushed and pulled things, and in the dead lift activity you lifted the weight using thread. In each case something needed to be pushed or pulled. When scientists talk about pushes and pulls, they use the word **force**. Scientists define forces as pushes and pulls.

You are now going to hold a conference with your classmates about the forces on the bucket and how the forces changed the bucket's motion. While you are discussing your ideas, make sure you use the word "force" when you talk about pushes and pulls.

During the demonstration, you may have discovered that there are a few things you already know about what makes things move. You probably also discovered that there are things you do not know yet. You are going to think of what you would like to investigate that might help you to answer the question, *What makes things move?*.

Develop two questions that might help you understand how objects move and what causes this motion. When you write your questions, keep in mind that your questions should:

- be interesting to you,
- require several resources to answer,
- relate to the *Big Question* and the crate-lift problem,
- require collecting and using data.

Make sure your question is not simply a yes/no question or one you can answer in one sentence.

When you have completed your two questions, meet with your small group. Share all the questions with each other. Carefully consider each question and decide if it meets the criteria for a good question. With your group, refine the questions that do not meet the criteria. Choose the two most interesting questions to share with the class. Give your teacher the rest of the questions so they might be used later.

Update the *Project Board*

You will now share your group's two questions with your class. Be prepared to support your questions with the criteria on the previous page. Your teacher will help you with the criteria if needed. Then your teacher will add your questions to the *Project Board*. Throughout this *Learning Set*, you will work to answer some of these questions.

Later in this *Learning Set*, you will conduct some investigations and use models to understand how forces work together on an object. The investigations will require you to make careful observations and record all your results. The *Project Board* can help you to organize your ideas as you answer the *Big Question*.

How do machines help move large, heavy objects?				
What do we think we know?	**What do we need to investigate?**	**What are we learning?**	**What is our evidence?**	**What does it mean for the challenge or question?**

1.2 Read

How Do Pushes and Pulls Relate to Force?

A force is being applied as the basketball player pushes down on the ball to bounce it.

A force is a push or pull. You apply a force to make an object move. There are many examples of things that you move in everyday life. Some of these examples include lifting a book to put it on the table, closing a door, dribbling a basketball, and lifting a trash bag to take out the garbage. To do each of these things, you have to apply a force. You push or pull something.

Think about the heavy-bucket demonstration. At the beginning of the demonstration, the bucket was sitting on the table. It was not moving. Scientists would say the bucket was *at rest*. When your teacher pushed and pulled the bucket very lightly, applying a small force, the bucket did not move. A force was applied, but it was not enough to make the bucket move. When your teacher applied a little more force, the bucket moved. Finally, your teacher applied a much larger force, and the bucket moved more.

In these demonstrations, a force was applied to move the heavy bucket. The bucket's motion was affected differently by greater amounts of force. With a small force, the motion did not change. The bucket stayed at rest. With more force, the bucket moved.

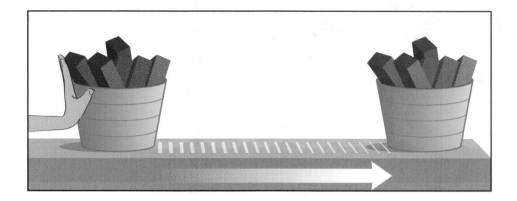

Forces can change motion. You need to apply forces to make things move and to make things stop moving. If a cart is moving across the floor, a force was needed to start it moving and a force is needed to make the cart stop moving.

Forces are also needed to change direction. When you want an object to turn you have to push or pull the object in the direction you want it to turn.

You do not just apply forces to get things moving. You also need to apply a force to make things stop, slow down, change direction, or change speed. For example, riding a skateboard is all about using forces. To start riding a skateboard and build up speed, the rider pushes off the ground with one foot. To change direction or turn a corner, the rider applies a force by pushing down more on one side of the board.

To start riding a skateboard and build up speed, the rider pushes off the ground with one foot. To change direction or turn a corner, the rider applies a force by pushing down more on one side of the board. A common way to slow down or stop a skateboard is to press down on the tail, or back, of the board until it drags on the pavement.

Moving a skateboard	
To stop the skateboard	Apply a force to the skateboard.
To speed the skateboard up	Apply a force to the skateboard. (Kick it.)
To change the skateboard's direction	Apply a force to one side of the skateboard.

To change the speed or direction of an object,
a force must be applied to the object.

Moving objects do not have any force of their own. Forces are a result of interactions between two objects. This interaction requires contact. For example, imagine that you are catching a baseball. As the ball is moving through the air, it does not have force. When the ball lands in your glove, the ball applies a force to your glove. You can feel it. Your glove also applies a force to the ball. This force slows the ball down and makes it stop moving. Neither the ball nor the glove had a force by itself. The force acts when the two objects interact. In this example, a force acts when the ball hits the glove.

Stop and Think

1. Give two examples of something you pushed and pulled today. Use different examples than those in the reading.

2. Compare the amount of force used to move the bucket with how much the bucket moved in each part of the demonstration.

3. When pushing the heavy bucket, what two objects interacted? Draw a picture of pushing the bucket. Make sure your picture includes all the objects that are interacting and the forces on the objects.

Force Diagrams

You drew a picture of the heavy bucket being pushed. You might have found it difficult to include all the information about forces in your picture. When scientists want to show the forces that are acting on an object, they use force diagrams.

Force diagrams provide a simple way to show the forces acting on an object. Instead of drawing the object, scientists simplify the object. Usually, the object will be shown as a square or other simple shape. Scientists then use arrows to show forces acting on the object. The direction of the arrow shows the direction of the force. You would show a push to the right with an arrow pointing to the right. The length of the arrow shows the size of the force. If two forces were the same size, the arrows would be the same length. If one force were twice as big as another, that arrow would be two times longer.

An example of a force diagram is shown below. The arrows are equal in length because the forces on the object are equal. The forces are acting in opposite directions so they are pointing in opposite directions. One force is pushing up, and the other force is pulling down.

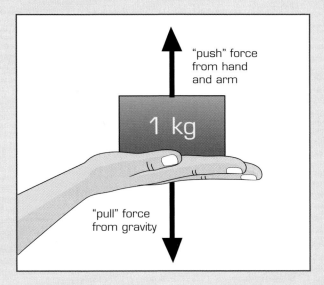

Stop and Think

Redraw your picture of the heavy bucket as a force diagram. Remember to indicate the direction and size of the forces.

What's the Point?

Forces cause objects to change motion. Forces can change the speed of an object, slowing it down or making it speed up. Forces can also change the direction of an object. Forces can make objects turn. When an object is moving, a small push or pull might not be enough to make an object change its speed or direction. It might be necessary to apply a lot of force to an object to make it change its motion.

Previously, you discussed the idea of lifting the crate from the beach to the top of the cliff. This *lift* could be a push or a pull depending upon how you build your machine. You will have to apply a force to move the crate. In the next section, you will learn more about the nature of that force.

Locomotives provide the force needed to move train cars. Locomotives move the train from the front. Sometimes locomotives are also used to push the train.

1.3 Investigate

How Do Forces Affect Motion?

In this *Learning Set*, you have been thinking about forces and motion. You now know that forces are pushes and pulls that act when two objects interact. Forces can be large or small. Next you will investigate the effect of various forces on the motion of a heavy object. You will use a science instrument called a "force probe" to measure the amount of force applied to the object when it is pushed or pulled.

In order to answer the question *What makes things move?* you are going to explore what happens in seven different situations. Each group will be assigned to do two of the explorations, and then the groups will report what they have observed to the class in an *Investigation Expo*. In each situation, a different force will be applied to a heavy object. For each situation, you will predict if the probes will measure the same or different amounts of force. You will first record your prediction of what you think will happen. A prediction is an educated guess based on what you know. You should not only record what you think will happen, but you should also record your reason for why you think it will happen.

Next, you will observe what actually happens. You will draw a diagram of your observations.

Finally, you will compare what you observed with what you predicted. When everyone has finished, you will share your observations with your class. Your class will work together to develop a statement describing the relationship between forces and motion.

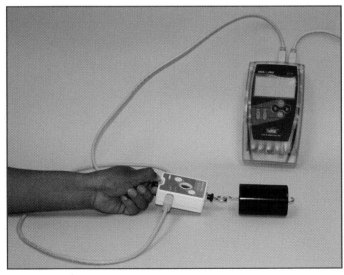

A force probe is an instrument used to measure the amount of force applied to an object.

newton: a unit used to measure force.

Measuring Force

In this investigation, you will be using force probes to measure the amount of force that is applied to an object. A force probe is a measuring device similar to a spring scale used to weigh things. The probe measures the amount of force applied using a unit called a **newton**. A newton (N) is a measure of force in the same way that a meter is a measure of distance and a second is a measure of time. If you are holding a mass of 1 kg (2.2 lbs), you are applying an upward force of about 10 N on the mass.

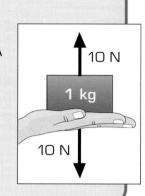

Procedure

1. **Situation 1**

   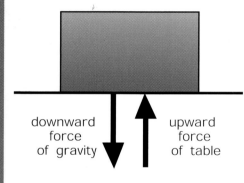

   a) Place a weight on your table.

   b) Predict how the motion of the weight will change if the weight is not touched. Record your prediction. You also need to record the reason why you made this prediction.

   c) Observe the weight for a short time and record your observation. Include a diagram to show the forces acting on the weight. Use a table similar to the following to record your data.

   d) Compare your observations with your predictions. How would you explain what happened in this situation?

Demonstration Notes Name_____ Date_____			
Demonstration	**Predict**	**Observe**	**Compare**
#1 Describe the event here.			
#2 Describe the event here.			
#3 Describe the event here.			

2. Situation 2

In this situation, you will be pushing on the weight with the same force from opposite sides of the weight. Read the directions carefully and use the force diagram to help you.

a) The weight is at rest on the table. Make a prediction about the motion of the weight. What do you think the change in motion will be if you push on the weight, equally, from opposite sides? Justify your prediction. Record your prediction and what you know that supports it.

b) Attach the force probes to the weight as shown in the photo on page 21. Push on the weight and use the force probe readings to make sure you are pushing with equal force.

c) Observe the motion of the weight. Record your observations. Use arrows on your diagram to show any motion of the weight.

d) Compare your observations with your predictions. How would you explain what happened in this situation?

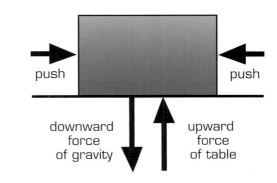

3. Situation 3

In this situation you will be pushing on the weight with the different forces from opposite sides of the weight. Read the directions carefully and use the force diagram to help you.

a) The weight is at rest on the table. Make a prediction about the motion of the weight. What do you think the change in motion will be if you push on the weight with more force from the left side of the weight? Justify your prediction. Record your prediction and what you know that supports it.

b) Attach the force probe to the weight as shown in the photo on page 21. Push on the weight and use the force probe readings to make sure you are pushing with different forces.

c) Observe the motion of the weight. Record your observations. Use arrows on your diagram to show any motion of the weight.

d) Compare your observations with your predictions. How would you explain what happened in this situation?

4. Situation 4

In this situation, you will be pulling on the weight with the same force from opposite sides of the weight. Read the directions carefully and use the force diagram to help you.

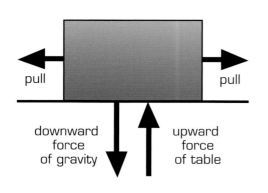

a) The weight is at rest on the table. Make a prediction about the motion of the weight. What do you think the change in motion will be if you pull on the weight, equally, from opposite sides? Justify your prediction. Record your prediction and what you know that supports it.

b) Attach the force probe to the weight as shown in the photo on page 21. Pull on the weight and use the force probe readings to make sure you are pulling with equal force.

c) Observe the motion of the weight. Record your observations. Use arrows on your diagram to show any motion of the weight.

d) Compare your observations with your predictions. How would you explain what happened in this situation?

5. Situation 5

In this situation, you will be pulling on the weight with different forces from opposite sides of the weight. Read the directions carefully and use the force diagram to help you.

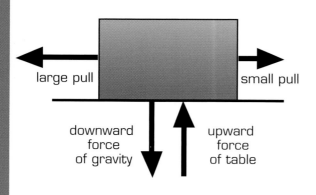

a) The weight is at rest on the table. Make a prediction about the motion of the weight. What do you think the change in motion will be if you pull on the weight with different forces, from opposite sides? Justify your prediction. Record your prediction and what you know that supports it.

b) Attach the force probe to the weight as shown in the photo on page 21. Push on the weight and use the force probe readings to make sure you are pushing with unequal forces.

c) Observe the motion of the weight. Record your observations. Use arrows on your diagram to show any motion of the weight.

d) Compare your observations with your predictions. How would you explain what happened in this situation?

6. Situation 6

In this situation, you pull up on the weight without removing it from the table. Read the directions carefully and use the force diagram to help you.

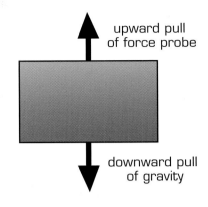

a) The weight is at rest on the table. What do you think the change in motion will be if you pull up on the weight with the force probe without lifting it off the table? Justify your prediction. Record your prediction and what you know that supports it.

b) Attach the force probe to the weight as shown in the photo on page 21. Pull on the weight as hard as you can without lifting it off the table.

c) What is the reading on the force probe?

d) Observe the motion of the weight. Record your observations. Use arrows on your diagram to show any motion of the weight.

e) Compare your observations with your predictions. How would you explain what happened in this situation?

7. Situation 7

In this situation, you pull up on the weight and lift it from the table. Read the directions carefully and use the force diagram to help you.

a) The weight is at rest on the table. What do you think the change in motion will be if you pull up on the weight with the force probe and lift it off the table? Justify your prediction. Record your prediction and what you know that supports it.

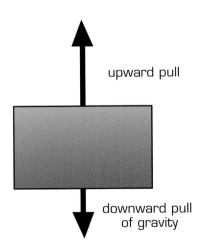

b) Attach the force probe to the weight as shown in the photo on page 21. Pull on the weight as needed to lift it off the table. Pull on the weight slowly so you can read the force on the probe.

c) What is the reading on the force probe as the weight is lifted from the table?

d) Observe the motion of the weight. Record your observations. Use arrows on your diagram to show any motion of the weight.

e) Compare your observations with your predictions. How would you explain what happened in this situation?

MOVING BIG THINGS

Communicate

Investigation Expo

Each group has explored two different situations. Create a poster that describes briefly what you did in each exploration and what you learned from it. Make sure that your ideas are described clearly so that the rest of your class can learn from your experiences. As you describe your understanding of your situations, be sure to use the scientific words you already know. Use the word *force* to describe the pushes and pulls on your object.

As you are listening to others' presentations, pay attention to how each of the situations is unique. Think about how the situations are different from the ones you explored. Note anything that surprises you.

Explain

Now that you have listened to everyone's description and ideas about their situations, you will create an explanation of the effect of various forces on how an object moves.

Create Your Explanation

Name:_____ Date:_____

Use this page to explain the lesson of your recent investigations.

Write a brief summary of the results from your investigation. You will use this summary to help you write your Explanation.

Claim – a statement of what you understand or a conclusion that you have reached from an investigation or a set of investigations.

Evidence – data collected during investigations and trends in that data.

Science knowledge – knowledge about how things work. You may have learned this through reading, talking to an expert, discussion, or other experiences.

Write your Explanation using the *Claim*, *Evidence* and *Science knowledge*.

Recall that a good explanation has this structure:

- your claim
- your evidence
- your science knowledge
- a logical statement tying the claim to the evidence in science

If you have created explanations before, you know that after scientists get results from an investigation they make a claim based on what their evidence shows. A claim is a statement of what you understand or a conclusion that you have reached from an investigation. You will do the same thing now based on the results of your investigation into force and motion. Using the *Create Your Explanation* page, develop a statement declaring your claim.

Next, you will state your evidence. Describe the data that support your claim. You may want to include force diagrams to help communicate this information.

Science knowledge is knowledge about how things work. This knowledge comes through reading, discussion, talking to an expert, or other experiences. You may include information that you read in this *Learning Set* or knowledge you have gained from other resources. Put this all together to write an explanation on your own. Do not worry if you cannot create a perfect explanation. Just work with the information you have for now. There will be opportunities for you to revisit and refine your explanation as you learn more.

With your group, take turns sharing explanations. Then work together to build a group explanation.

Communicate

Share Your Explanation

Your class will meet to discuss each group's explanation. Your teacher will guide the class toward selecting or creating the explanation that everyone thinks best explains the relationship between force and motion.

What's the Point?

The forces acting on an object can change the way an object moves. Forces can make an object speed up, slow down, or change direction. The investigations in this section showed what happens to an object when different forces act on it. Your explanation helped describe how the forces acting on an object can change the object's motion.

To lift weights, you must apply an upward force on the weights greater than the downward force of gravity on the weights.

1.4 Read

What are Balanced and Unbalanced Forces?

balanced forces: forces that are equal in size and opposite in direction. When forces are balanced, there is no change in motion.

unbalanced forces: forces applied to an object in opposite directions that are not equal in size. Unbalanced forces result in a change of motion.

friction: the force that opposes the motion of two objects that are in contact.

In the last section, you experienced pushing and pulling on an object with equal and unequal forces. In some of the situations, you noticed that the weight did not move. In some of the situations, the weight moved. Your explanation and discussion with your class helped you understand what makes objects move. In this reading, you will learn more about the forces on an object when the motion of an object does not change. This is when forces are **balanced**. When the motion of an object changes, the forces are **unbalanced**.

Balanced Forces

Balanced forces are equal in size and opposite in direction. When forces are balanced, there is no change in motion. In one of your situations in the last section, you pushed or pulled on an object from opposite directions but with the same force. You observed that the object did not move. When the forces on an object are equal and in opposite directions, the forces are balanced and there is no change in motion.

Remember when the heavy bucket in your classroom was pushed lightly? It was standing still, or at rest. Although a force was applied to it, the bucket remained at rest. Its motion did not change. The forces acting on the bucket were balanced. It was pushed in one direction, but a different force, called **friction**, pushed back in the opposite direction. The two forces were equal in size and opposite in direction so they cancelled each other out and no motion occurred.

In the investigation, you applied balanced forces to a heavy object. You pushed on the object with the same amount of force from opposite sides. The force probes measured the amount of force that you applied on each side. You saw that the forces were the same. You also pulled on the object with the same amount of force in opposite directions. The force probes showed that the forces were equal. In both cases, you observed that the motion of the object did not change. It stayed at rest and did not move.

Another example of balanced forces can be seen in the game tug-of-war. In this game, the same number of people hold onto each end of a rope. A flag is tied to the center of the rope. Each team pulls on the rope and tries to move the flag to its side.

Imagine that you are playing tug-of-war with your friends. Your team starts by pulling really hard, with all its strength. But the other team is also pulling with an equal amount of force and in the opposite direction. The flag in the middle of the rope does not move. The flag does not move because the force that your team is pulling with is equal to the force applied by the other team, but in the opposite direction. The forces are in opposite directions. The forces on the rope are balanced. When the forces are balanced, the flag in the center of the rope will not move. To win the game, one team must apply more force than the other.

Children playing tug-of-war

Gravity

In the *Situation 1* in the previous section, you observed a weight sitting on the table. The force diagram for this situation shows the force of gravity pulling on the weight and the table pushing back on the weight. The arrows are the same size showing that the forces are the same size. The arrows also show that the forces are acting in opposite directions. Because the forces are the same size and acting in opposite directions, the forces are balanced. There is no change in motion for the object.

When you lifted the weight in the air in *Situation 7*, you had to use some force. Then you had to maintain that force to keep the weight in the air.

You may have felt that you were just holding the object but you were applying a *pulling force* upward. The weight did not move because there was an equal pulling force working opposite your force, pulling the weight down. The downward force is **gravity**.

Gravity is the force that pulls everything towards Earth. When an object is being held in the air, the force holding it up must balance the force of gravity pulling it down. To hold a bag of groceries you must pull up with a force equal to the downward force of gravity.

In the first situation in the last section, you observed a weight as it sat on the table. You probably noted that without any forces being applied to it, the weight didn't move. You could have watched the weight for hours, but as long as there were no further pushes or pulls on the weight, it would not have moved. The forces on the weight were balanced and there was no change in motion.

The force diagram for the first situation showed two force arrows, one down and one up, both the same size. These arrows represent the forces acting on the object. The downward force shows the force of gravity. The upward force is the force of the table on the weight.

gravity: the force that pulls everything towards Earth.

Friction

Remember when your teacher pushed the heavy bucket lightly? It was at rest sitting on the table, and it remained at rest when it was pushed lightly. Although a force was applied to it, the bucket remained at rest. Its motion did not change. The forces acting on the bucket were balanced. The push acted on the bucket in one direction but another force acted on the bucket in the opposite direction. The force that acted against the push was friction.

Friction is a force that opposes the motion of two objects that are in contact. In the case of the heavy bucket, there was friction between the bucket and the surface it was sitting on.

Friction was the force opposing the motion of the bucket. It balanced out the small force that was applied to the bucket. To move the bucket you had to apply a force strong enough to overcome the force of friction.

Friction acts to resist motion. When you push on the bucket, friction acts to keep the bucket from moving.

Unbalanced Forces

When forces on an object are balanced, there is no change in motion. So what do you need to do to move something? If something starts to move, it must be because unbalanced forces are acting on it.

To have unbalanced forces means that the force applied in one direction is greater than the force applied in the opposite direction. When unbalanced forces are acting on an object, there is a change in speed and direction.

When you pushed lightly on the bucket in the class demonstration, it did not move. It only moved when you pushed on it hard enough. To move the bucket, the force you applied had to be greater than the friction force acting in the opposite direction. One force (pushing) had to be greater than the other force (friction) before the bucket would move. When one force is greater than another, the forces are not balanced. Instead, they are unbalanced.

By applying an unbalanced force you can change the motion of an object. Unbalanced forces can make an object at rest start moving, make a moving object stop, or change the direction and speed of the object.

Think back to the game of tug-of-war. At the start of the game, both teams pulled equally hard on opposite ends of the rope. The two teams pulled with balanced forces. The flag in the middle of the rope did not move.

After a while one team begins to get tired. It pulls with less force. The other team becomes excited and pulls with even more force. This team pulls and

MOVING BIG THINGS

For a team to win a game of tug-of-war, it must pull with greater force than the other team.

pulls. Soon the tired team is moving in the direction that the stronger team is pulling. The flag moves. The stronger team wins!

What happened during the game? The flag in the middle of the rope moved toward the stronger team because there were unbalanced forces acting on the rope. The force applied by the stronger team was greater than the force applied by the tired team. When the forces became unbalanced, the flag started to move in the direction of the greater force. That direction was towards the stronger team, so they won!

In one of your situations, you pushed on an object unequally and in opposite directions. In this situation, the forces were unbalanced. The object moved across the table in the direction of the greater force. You also pulled on the object with different amounts of force and in opposite directions. The object moved in the direction of the greater pulling force. You drew diagrams for each situation. Your diagrams may look something like the ones shown.

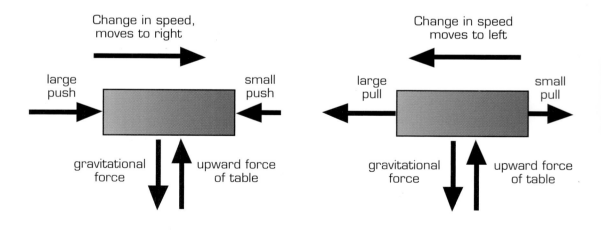

In these diagrams, the arrows represent the direction of the forces that you applied to the object. The arrows are different sizes because you pushed and pulled on the object with different amounts of force. When the object moved across the table. The arrows above the object shows the direction of the motion. The object moved because you applied unbalanced forces.

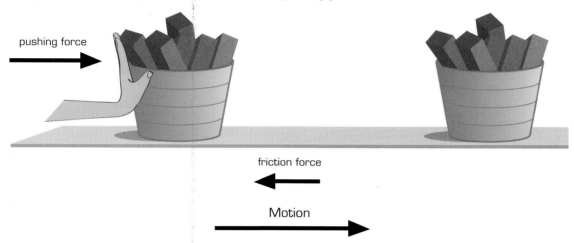

pushing force

friction force

Motion

Pushing against friction with unbalanced forces

A similar situation occurred when your teacher pushed the heavy bucket. With a small push, the bucket did not move. The friction force balanced the small pushing force. When a larger force was applied, the bucket moved. The pushing force was now greater than the friction force. Since the forces were unbalanced, the bucket moved.

Stop and Think

1. Suppose you were pushing on a heavy bucket of stones with 100 N of force and it did not move. How many newtons of force would be balancing the force you were applying?

2. You need to push a very heavy rock. You push and push but the rock doesn't move. Create a force diagram that shows how the forces work as you are pushing on the rock.

3. A strong adult pulls a desk to the right. At the same time, a small child pulls the desk to the left. Draw a force diagram of this situation. What direction will the desk move? Why do you think it will move in that direction?

4. When an apple falls from a tree forces must be acting on it. Create a force diagram and describe how the forces act on the apple to make it fall.

What's the Point?

Forces acting on objects occur in pairs and are either balanced or unbalanced. When a pair of forces have equal strength and act in opposite directions, they are balanced forces. These two forces cancel each other out and the motion of the object they are acting on is unchanged.

When one of the forces in a pair is greater than the other, they are unbalanced. An unbalanced force results in a change in motion. For example, when an unbalanced force acts on an object at rest it will begin to move. An unbalanced force may also cause a moving object to stop, change direction, or change speed.

Friction is a force that resists motion when two objects are in contact. Gravity is the force that pulls everything toward Earth.

Friction and gravity are two forces that often act in the opposite direction of pushes and pulls.

In order to lift an object, a lifting force has to be applied that is greater than the pull of gravity.

Learning Set 1

Back to the Big Question

How do machines help move large, heavy objects?

Think back to the construction site or video that you saw at the beginning of this Unit. You and your classmates discussed what each of the different types of machines might be used for. Large objects such as heavy metal beams, large piles of bricks, and big piles of dirt are difficult to move. That is because there are large forces of gravity and friction acting on them. It is not possible for people to move such heavy objects by themselves. A machine is able to apply a larger force than a person can. The machine can apply a force greater than the force of gravity or friction on the large, heavy object. Since the applied force is greater, there are unbalanced forces acting on the object. The object's motion changes. This is why people use machines to help them move big things.

Machines can be designed to move specific objects. For example, a bulldozer is designed to push dirt from one place to another, so it applies an unbalanced force along the ground. A backhoe is designed to dig holes, so it applies unbalanced forces downward to scoop up the dirt and then upward to lift it out of the hole. Smaller machines are designed the same way. A hammer, for instance, is designed to push a nail through wood. It applies a large unbalanced force to the head of the nail. A pair of scissors applies an unbalanced force to a very small point on a piece of paper, allowing the scissors to cut.

A hammer applies a large unbalanced force on the top of a nail to move the nail into the wood.

Explore

In this Unit, you determined the number of threads required to lift the weight to the top of the cliff. Maybe you found that it requires six or seven threads to avoid having the threads break. You could make the argument that each of these threads represents a certain amount of upward lifting force. You had to create a situation where the forces were unbalanced in the upward direction.

If these six or seven threads each represent a unit of force, the force of gravity must be equal to somewhere around five or six threads. You do not, however, measure force in *threads*. You measure force in newtons. Small forces can be measured with a device known as a *spring scale*.

Obtain a spring scale, the weight, and a loop of thread from before. Attach each of these to the spring scale and measure

- the amount of force required to lift the weight
- the amount of force the thread can handle just before it snaps.

These two numbers will be very important to you when you design your machine to help the biologists, Drs. Enrique, Susan, and Tanika. The measurement of the weight will tell you how much force is pulling down on the weight.

You learned during this *Learning Set* that the biologists need to create an unbalanced upward force to lift the crate up the cliff. You and your group have to do the same thing to the weight. Remember though, you only can use one single thread to apply the force to the weight. The difference between the force needed to lift the weight and the force at which the thread broke shows you how much force you will need to lift the weight. The machine you design will help supply that force.

In the next few *Learning Sets* you will learn how a machine might be able to help you make up the difference between these two force measurements.

Update the *Project Board*

Your teacher may have your class return to your *Project Board* to update any questions or ideas you have posted. You now can post some information in the *What are we learning?* column. Be sure to give the evidence you collected to support what you say you have learned about forces and how objects move.

Learning Set 2

How Can a Machine Change a Force?

Your challenge is to design a model of a machine that will help the biologists, Drs. Enrique, Susan, and Tanika, lift their supply crate from the beach up to the top of the cliff. In *Learning Set 1*, you discovered that you must generate a force larger than the weight of the crate to move it up the cliff. However, by themselves, the biologists can only supply a small amount of force to lift the crate. This force is too small to move the crate up the cliff.

To lift the crate, you will need to make up the difference between this small force and the force of gravity pulling down on the crate. How can you do this? In this *Learning Set,* you will learn how a machine can help a small force move big things.

The pictures show some large structures typically found in large cities—a high-rise building, a baseball stadium, and a bridge. These structures were obviously built with parts that a human would not be able to lift or move. As you saw on your construction walk, or in the construction video, people use machines to build structures such as these. When a person applies a small force to a machine, the machine applies a much larger force. The machine can apply a force large enough to move or lift something very heavy. In this *Learning Set,* you will find out how machines are able to do this.

2.1 Understand the Question

Thinking about How Machines Change Force

A machine can help move a heavy or large object. A machine, or maybe more than one machine, may help the scientists lift the heavy crate from the beach to the cliff. Your investigations in the last *Learning Set* showed how forces cause objects to move by changing their speed and/or direction. In this *Learning Set*, you will focus on how different machines can change force to make it possible to move big things.

Large machines used in construction often have many moving parts.

Types of Machines

Scientists have a very specific definition for machine. A machine changes the amount and/or direction of a force that can be applied to an object. This change makes it easier to move things.

At the construction site, you may have seen many large construction machines. These machines are large and elaborate. They have many moving parts. At the construction site, there were also smaller machines. You might not have seen these unless you were close enough. These smaller machines are usually called tools. Hammers, saws, and screwdrivers are three examples of handheld machines that have no moving parts. Like large construction machines, they make it easier for people to move things. This makes them machines as well.

There are machines that are used for other tasks besides building things. Some machines are used to help movers lift and move heavy items. Other machines make it easier for you to do everyday things. For example, think about a box tied up with string or ribbon. It can sometimes be difficult to break string or ribbon with your hands. It is much easier to use a pair of scissors. Scissors are a type of everyday machine.

Machines are needed to move large, heavy objects.

MOVING BIG THINGS

Scissors are an example of a machine that makes everyday tasks easier.

Pencil sharpeners are everyday machines too. Rakes, shovels, and wheelbarrows are also machines. So are spatulas you use for baking, spoons you use for stirring when you cook, forks and knives you use when you eat, and even your toothbrush. These are the types of machines that make everyday tasks easy to do.

There are many types of machines and they do very different kinds of things. It may be hard at first to see how construction machines, handheld machines, and everyday machines can be alike. They all make doing everyday and heavy tasks easier.

Stop and Think

1. Why do people use machines to help them build things?

2. Pick one of the following tasks. Describe the machines you might use in completing the task. Write the number of moving parts your machines have next to the name of the machine.

   a) building a birdhouse

   b) making a poster for school

   c) planting a garden

   d) moving a large rock

3. Write a short paragraph describing one morning in your life if there were no machines. Include details such as brushing your teeth, making your breakfast, and going to school or playing outside. Describe what you have to do each time you do not have the usual machine available to make the task easier for you.

Conference

You have read about different types of machines. You probably have some questions about how these machines can change a force. On your own, record two questions that might help you understand how a machine can change a force. When you write your questions, keep in mind that your questions should

- be interesting to you

- require several resources to answer

- relate to the big question and the crate-lift problem

- require collecting and using data

Remember to avoid yes/no questions and those that require only a one-sentence answer.

When you have completed your two questions, take the questions back to your small group. Share all the questions with each other. Carefully consider each question. Decide if it meets the criteria for a good question. With your group, refine the questions that do not meet the criteria. Choose the two most interesting questions to share with the class. Give your teacher the rest of the questions so they might be used later.

Update the *Project Board*

You may have already studied machines and know something about them. You also just read about several different types of machines. Discuss with your class what you think you know about machines. Record this in the *What do we think we know?* column.

Next, share your two questions with the class. Be prepared to support your questions with the criteria for a good question. During your classroom discussion, your teacher or one of the students will record each group's questions on the *Project Board*. These will go in the *What do we need to investigate?* column. Be sure to keep track of what is being recorded on your own *Project Board* page.

What's the Point?

In this Unit, you are trying to answer the question, *How do machines move large, heavy objects?*. To answer that question, you first had to become familiar with what a machine is. In this section, you discovered that there are many machines that are used to do many different tasks. These tasks may be quite small or very big. No matter how large or small a job, there is usually a machine that will make it easier to do!

What have you noticed about all of the machines you have become familiar with? They have one thing in common. Do you know what that is? If you compare them, some are very large and some are very small. Some are very simple and others more complex. However, all of them, regardless of size or shape, make doing the jobs they were designed for easier. When you learn how they do this, it will make it much easier for you to design your own machine to help the biologists move the crate to the top of the cliff.

More to Learn

Isaac Newton and Newton's Laws of Motion

You see pushes and pulls happening all around you, all the time. As a student scientist, you might wonder why an object moves or falls. You have many resources available to find the answer. However, in the early 1600s, people did not have such resources to turn to. There were a few great thinkers who observed the world around them and developed ideas about how and why things happen.

One of these people was the Italian philosopher Galileo Galilei (1564-1642). From his observations of a ball rolling down one ramp and up to an equal height on another ramp, he formed the "Principle of Inertia":

Inertia is the natural tendency of an object to remain at rest or to remain moving with constant speed in a straight line.

Sir Isaac Newton is considered by many to be one of the greatest scientific intellects. He is quoted as saying, "If I have been able to see further, it was only because I stood on the shoulders of giants."

In 1642, a year after Galileo's death, Isaac Newton was born in Woolsthorpe, England. Newton was a mathematician, physicist, and astronomer. A story is often told that Newton was in his orchard thinking about the Moon and its orbit when an apple fell. Newton wondered if the same force that makes an apple fall to the ground could hold the Moon in its orbit. This force, of course, was gravity. Whether the story is true or not, within a short time, Newton had developed early versions of what would become his three laws of motion.

In 1687, he published a book called *Principia*. The book included Newton's three laws of motion. These laws have many applications.

Newton's First Law of Motion

In the absence of an unbalanced force, an object at rest remains at rest, and an object already in motion remains in motion with constant speed in a straight-line path.

You may recognize this as an important idea you have learned in this Unit. You also may recognize this as the Principle of Inertia developed earlier by Galileo. Newton had read the work of Galileo and built on it. He included Galileo's Principle of Inertia as part of his First Law of Motion.

You have seen Newton's First Law of Motion in the investigations in this Unit. In *Learning Set 1*, you observed a weight on the table. You noticed that the weight did not move. You know that the weight will not move unless an unbalanced force acts on it. It would need to be pushed or pulled to move. This is exactly what Newton's law predicts will happen.

Newton's Second Law of Motion provides a way to figure out exactly how much force will be needed to change the speed or direction of an object.

Newton's Second Law of Motion

The acceleration of an object is directly proportional to the unbalanced force acting on it and is inversely proportional to the object's mass. The direction of the acceleration is the same as the direction of the unbalanced force.

The harder you pushed on the weight, the more the motion of the weight changed. This is an example of Newton's Second law.

Newton's Third Law of Motion

For every applied force, there is an equal and opposite force.

Newton's Third Law explains that forces come in pairs. You learned about pairs of forces in this Unit. When the weight is at rest on the table, it is pushing down on the table, and the table is pushing back on the weight with an equal force. The forces are equal but are in opposite directions.

You may have heard people refer to Isaac Newton as Sir Isaac Newton. His contributions to mathematics and science were so important that he was made a knight by Queen Anne in 1705.

These Laws of Motion are very complex, and this Unit only covers them a little. You will have a chance to learn more about Newton's Laws of Motion later this school year or in other science classes.

2.2 Investigate

How Do Inclined Planes Do Their Job?

It is much easier to take a car up to the top of a roller coaster using an inclined plane than to lift it straight to the top.

The most basic types of machines are called **simple machines**. They are called simple because they have very few, if any, moving parts. Once you understand how simple machines do their job, you can apply your knowledge to create a way for the biologists to lift the crate of supplies.

The first type of simple machine you will investigate is an **inclined plane**. This simple machine can help you lift things that might be too heavy to lift. You have seen many examples of inclined planes and probably call them ramps. An inclined plane is a ramp. The steepness, or slope, of the inclined plane changes how easy it is to move an object.

In this investigation, you will answer the question: ***How do inclined planes of varying steepness help you move an object?***

> **simple machine:** a machine with few or no moving parts.
>
> **inclined plane:** a sloping surface connecting a higher level to a lower level.

Predict

Describe how you think an inclined plane will help lift the weight. How do you think the steepness of the inclined plane will affect the results?

Procedure

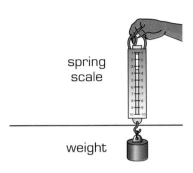

spring
scale

weight

Part 1: Lifting the Weight without an Inclined Plane

In this part, you will be lifting the weight 20 cm from the top of the table. Use the ruler to measure the height accurately. Use the spring scale to measure the force in newtons (N) needed to lift the weight off the table.

1. Use the diagram to help you set up your equipment correctly.

2   Attach the spring scale to the weight. Lift the weight 20 cm above the table using the spring scale. Measure the 20 cm from the top of the table to the bottom of the weight.

Materials
• spring scale
• metric ruler
• weight
• inclined plane

3. The amount of force you used to lift the weight is shown on the spring scale. Read the amount of force in newtons (N) you used to lift the weight. Record that measurement on your data table. (See the sample data after the *Procedure*.)

4. On the data table, record the distance the weight moved as 20 cm.

5. Repeat this procedure in the same way two more times for a total of three trials. Record all the data on your data table.

You have now lifted the weight to see how much force you need to lift the weight straight up from the table. This weight was not too heavy to lift. Some weights, like the crate on the beach, are very heavy. Use the next two parts of this procedure to see how the inclined plane can help move the weight.

Part 2: Lifting the Weight Using the Steepest Inclined Plane

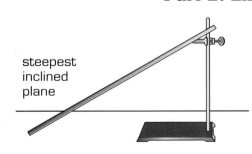

steepest
inclined
plane

In this part, you will be using an inclined plane at the steepest position to lift the weight up 20 cm. The height will stay constant. Therefore, you will be able to compare your force data to the force data for just lifting the weight straight off the table.

1. See the diagram to help you set up your equipment correctly. The inclined plane should be in the steepest position. Put the ruler next to the inclined plane and measure 20 cm in height. Hold the ruler at this position.

2. Place the weight on the cart. Attach the spring scale to the cart. Set the cart and weight at the bottom of the inclined plane. The wheels should be on the ramp.

3. Pull the cart and weight up the ramp using the spring scale. Stop when the back of the cart reaches a vertical height of 20 cm off the table.

4. The amount of force you used to pull the weight is shown on the spring scale. Read the amount of force you used to pull the weight. Record that measurement on your data table.

5. Use the ruler to measure how far up the ramp the cart moved. Start at the bottom of the ramp and measure to the back of the cart on the ramp. On the data table, record the distance the weight moved up the inclined plane.

6. Repeat this procedure in the same way two more times for a total of three trials. Record all the data on your data table.

Part 3: Lifting the Weight Using Less-Steep Inclined Planes

In this part, you will lower the steepness of your inclined plane. Use the same procedure as in *Part 2* but with less-steep inclined planes.

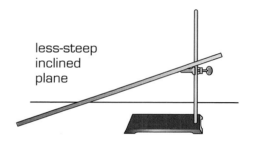

less-steep inclined plane

1. Use the diagram to help you set up your equipment correctly. The inclined plane should be in a less-steep position. Put the ruler next to the inclined plane and measure 20 cm in height. Hold the ruler at this position.

2. Attach the spring scale to the cart. Set the cart and weight at the bottom of the inclined plane. The wheels should be on the ramp

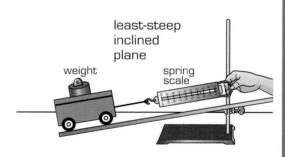

least-steep inclined plane

weight

spring scale

3. Pull the cart and weight up the ramp using the spring scale. Stop when the back of the cart reaches a vertical height of 20 cm off the table.

4. The amount of force you used to pull the weight is shown on the spring scale. Read the amount of force you used to pull the weight. Record that measurement on your data table.

5. Use the ruler to measure how far up the ramp the cart moved. Start at the bottom of the ramp and measure to the back of the cart. On the data table, record the distance the weight moved up the inclined plane.

6. Repeat this procedure in the same way two more times for a total of three trials. Record all the data on your data table.

7. Again, lower the inclined plane's steepness. Repeat *Steps 1* through *6* above.

Recording Your Data

Use the following tables to record your data from each trial.

Vertical lift		Steepest inclined plane		Less-steep inclined plane		Least-steep inclined plane	
Force to lift weight (N)	Distance weight is lifted (cm)	Force to pull weight (N)	Distance weight is pulled (cm)	Force to pull weight (N)	Distance weight is pulled (cm)	Force to pull weight (N)	Distance weight is pulled (cm)

Vertical lift		Steepest inclined plane		Less-steep inclined plane		Least-steep inclined plane	
Average force to lift weight (N)	Average distance weight is lifted (cm)	Average force to pull weight (N)	Average distance weight is pulled (cm)	Average force to pull weight (N)	Average distance weight is pulled (cm)	Average force to pull weight (N)	Average distance weight is pulled (cm)

Analyze Your Data

Use the averages of your data. Graph the results for force and distance. Be sure to label the vertical axes using the appropriate units.

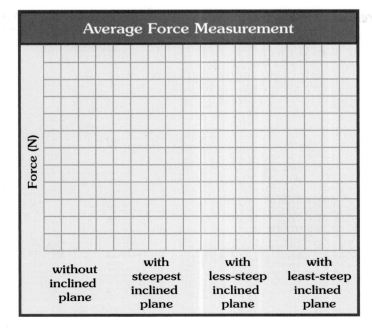

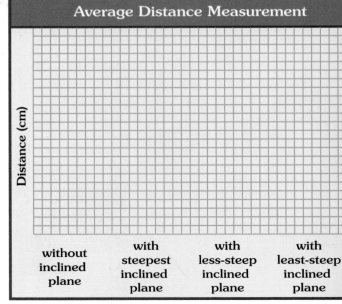

Communicate Your Results

Investigation Expo

Scientists present their procedures and results to each other. You will now share your procedures and results with your class in an *Investigation Expo*. To prepare for this, make a poster that answers these questions.

- What question were you trying to answer in the investigation?

- What was your predicted outcome?

- What procedure did you use and do you feel it was a fair test?

- What materials did you use?

- You noticed some trends in the data. Report the trends you noticed. If you had difficulty finding the trends, tell your class why you think it was difficult to find the trends. Describe changes in your procedure that you think might help you get more accurate results.

- What is your interpretation?

- Identify the variables you controlled and those you changed.

Remember it is important to report the procedure you used in your investigation. Each group might run their investigations a little differently. You might want to begin constructing your poster as you move through the investigation, adding information and data along the way.

Because everyone did the same investigation, during this *Investigation Expo*, only a few of the groups will present their results. Instead, you will place your posters on the wall and have a chance to see each one, but only two or three groups will present.

As you look at the other posters, examine them closely to see if you can answer this set of questions from each poster.

- What variables did they control as they did their procedure?

- How did the group make sure that they measured the force used to pull the weight up the inclined plane consistently?

- How are the results of this group similar to your results? How are they different? What did this group do in its experiment that would make its results different from yours?

After looking at the posters, your class will discuss the answers to these questions. You will also talk about what you have learned from your investigations about inclined planes.

Apply

The United States government requires buildings to allow access to all people. All buildings are now built to be handicapped accessible. One way to make buildings more accessible is to use ramps to help people who use wheelchairs enter the building more easily.

1. Using what you just learned about inclined planes, describe how a ramp could be a help to someone who uses a wheelchair.

2. You are designing a building.

    a) What type of ramp would you put on the entrance to the building to allow a person on a wheelchair the easiest access possible?

    b) What are some everyday problems that might be related to your ramp solution?

3. Suppose you were adding a wheelchair ramp to an existing building and only had a small amount of space available for the ramp. What could you do to make the ramp safe and easy to use?

What's the Point?

In these investigations, you controlled the height you raised the weight above the table. You measured the force used to pull the weight and the distance you pulled it on the inclined plane. You recorded, averaged, and graphed all that information.

You have collected and shared a lot of data about how inclined planes change the force needed to raise a weight above a table. You have seen that as the inclined plane gets steeper, the force needed to raise the weight goes up. You have also seen that as the inclined plane gets steeper, the distance you must move the weight is less.

2.3 Explain

Create an Explanation of How an Inclined Plane Does its Job

After scientists get results from an investigation, they try to make a claim. They base their claims on evidence. They may also use what they already know to explain why their claim is valid. The purpose of a science explanation is to help others understand what was learned from a set of investigations and how the scientist reached this conclusion.

Later, other scientists will use these explanations to help them explain other phenomena. The explanations will also help them predict what will happen in other situations.

Create Your Explanation

Name:_____ Date:_____

Use this page to explain the lesson of your recent investigations.

> Write a brief summary of the results from your investigation. You will use this summary to help you write your Explanation.

> **Claim** – a statement of what you understand or a conclusion that you have reached from an investigation or a set of investigations.

> **Evidence** – data collected during investigations and trends in that data.

> **Science knowledge** – knowledge about how things work. You may have learned this through reading, talking to an expert, discussion, or other experiences.

> Write your Explanation using the *Claim*, *Evidence* and *Science knowledge*.

You will develop an explanation now. Your claim will be the trend you found in your inclined plane investigation. You will use data you collected and previous science knowledge you have to create a good explanation. It should describe how the applied force changes as the steepness of the inclined plane changes. You should also detail any relationship between the force applied to the weight and the distance the weight must be moved to get it to where it needs to be.

Because your understanding of the science of forces and inclined planes is not complete, you may not be able to write a full explanation. Do your best based on what you understand now. As you learn more, you can make your explanation better.

Explain

Recall that an explanation is made up of three parts:

- Claim—a statement of what you understand or a conclusion that you have reached from an investigation or set of investigations

- Evidence—data collected during investigations and trends in that data

- Science knowledge—knowledge about how things work. You may have learned this through reading, talking to an expert, discussion, or other experiences.

An explanation is a statement that connects the claim to the evidence and science knowledge in a logical way. A good explanation will convince somebody that the claim is valid.

Do your best to explain the results of your investigation. Meet with your group to write an explanation of how the steepness of an inclined plane affects the force needed to move an object. The *Create Your Explanation* page provides hints so that you'll remember how to put an explanation together.

Communicate

Share Your Explanation

When everyone is finished, you will share your explanations with the class. As each group shares theirs, record each explanation. You might also create a poster for the classroom that has the full set of explanations on it. You will have an opportunity to revise your explanations after you learn more about how inclined planes work.

What's the Point?

Scientists make claims about the phenomena they investigate. They support their claims with evidence gathered during investigations. They also read reports that others have written based on their investigations. They combine all of that together to create explanations of their claims. Other people carefully examine these explanations and determine whether the claims are trustworthy.

Your class has completed an investigation of how a simple machine can affect how much force needs to be applied to move something. You now know how inclined planes help to reduce the force you need to apply to move an object. You also noticed that the distance you had to move the object changed when different inclined planes were used. Your explanation was a first attempt at describing the relationship between the force that had to be applied and the distance the object had to be moved. In the next section, you will learn more about this relationship. Then you will have a chance to revise your explanation.

2.4 Read

How Does an Inclined Plane Help to Move Big Things?

trade-off: the giving up of one thing in exchange for another.

mechanical advantage: the amount a machine increases the force applied to an object. As a trade-off, the distance that the object must be moved is increased.

Mechanical Advantage

You investigated one type of simple machine—the inclined plane. When you used the inclined plane, you used less force to move the weight to 20 cm than you used to lift the weight vertically. You also noticed that there is a **trade-off**. You have to give up one thing in exchange for another. The trade-off for the inclined plane is that to use less force to lift the weight, you actually had to pull the weight a longer distance. This trade-off applies to all machines. It is called **mechanical advantage**.

The purpose of any machine—large or small—is to change the amount of force required to move something or to change the direction in which the force is applied. The machine gives you an advantage, or benefit. Machines that put out more force than what is put into them are said to have a mechanical advantage. Every simple machine has a mechanical advantage. Remember when you lifted the weight vertically. You had to move the spring scale 20 cm to get the weight to move 20 cm. The mechanical advantage is one because the distance the weight moved divided by the distance your hand moved is one.

The mechanical advantage for machines is usually more than one. For example, think about the inclined planes you investigated. You noticed that as you lowered the inclined plane you had to pull over a longer distance to lift the cart 20 cm above the table. Although you pulled with less force, you pulled over a greater distance.

The mechanical advantage of an inclined plane is more than one. The mechanical advantage of an inclined plane is found by dividing the distance you pulled by the height of the inclined plane. If you pulled the weight up the inclined plane 40 cm to raise the weight 20 cm, your mechanical advantage would be 40 cm divided by 20 cm or 2. Although you had to exert half the force, you had to do it over a distance twice as long. You do not have to remember this formula but it is useful to know that there is a relationship. That relationship is called mechanical advantage.

Other Inclined Planes

The Wedge

The wedge can be a type of simple machine used to cut or split things. It is a variation of the inclined plane. A wedge is a single inclined plane or two inclined planes placed together as shown in the diagram. A wedge reduces the amount of force needed to move something. A wedge also changes the direction of the applied force.

A wood splitter is an example of a wedge. When a downward force is applied to the flat part of a wood splitter, the wood splitter directs that force so that it pushes out to both sides. The wood is pushed apart on the two sides of the wedge.

A knife is another example of a wedge. When you use a knife to cut an apple, the blade of the knife directs the downward force you apply sideways. The sideways force pushes apart the pieces of the apple.

Wedges that are thinner have a greater mechanical advantage than thicker wedges. This is why cutting tools work best when they are sharpened.

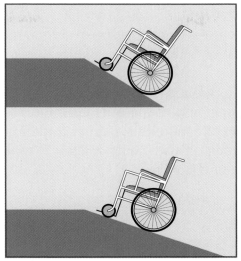

It takes less force to push the wheelchair up the less-steep ramp than the steeper ramp. However, the distance over which the force needs to be applied is greater for the less-steep ramp than the steeper one.

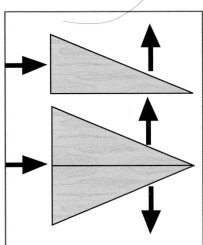

Imagine how impossible it would be to split apart a piece of wood using just the force you could apply with your hands.

The Screw

The screw is another type of simple machine. Like the wedge, it is also a variation of an inclined plane. It is an inclined plane wrapped around a cylinder. Think of the common screw. The thread that wraps around the screw is the inclined plane. Like the wedge, a screw increases the force you apply and changes its direction. The screw changes a small force in a turning direction into a larger force in the direction you are pointing it. The trade-off with using a screw is that you have to apply the force through a greater distance.

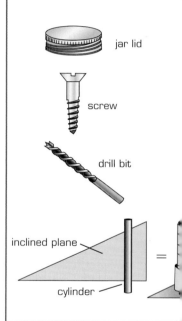

jar lid

screw

drill bit

inclined plane

cylinder

=

If you look at a set of screws, you will see that the threads on some screws are wide apart. On others, they are close together. The wider apart the threads are, the "steeper" the inclined plane. It is easier to put in a screw with threads that are closer together than one with threads that are farther apart. However, you will have to make many more turns of a screw with very close threads.

Other examples of screws used in daily life include a drill bit and threads on twist-on bottle caps.

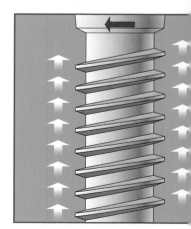

Project-Based Inquiry Science

Stop and Think

1. A wedge is a special example of an inclined plane. Draw a picture of a wedge and show where the inclined planes are. Describe when you might use a wedge to help you.

2. Suppose you had to put a screw into a piece of wood and had only a handheld screw driver. Which type of screw would you prefer to use? Support your answer with evidence. Use mechanical advantage and force in your answer

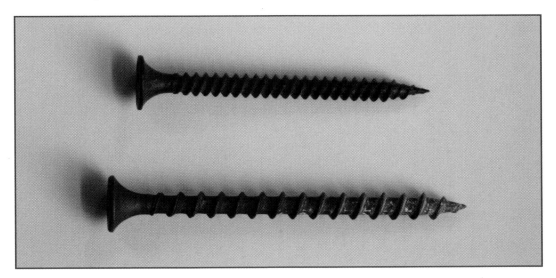

What's the Point?

Machines can help you move heavy objects by changing the amount or direction of the applied force. However, there is always a trade-off when you use a machine. A trade-off means that in order to get something you want, you have to give up something. If you want to apply less force to move something, you have to apply the force through a greater distance. This trade-off for machines is called the *mechanical advantage* of the machine.

When using machines there is always a trade-off. A machine might allow you to use less force to move something but you will have to move it over a greater distance. This trade-off is called mechanical advantage.

2.5 Revise Your Explanation

How Does an Inclined Plane Do Its Job?

Explanation

Machines can transform a small applied force into a large force. The trade-off is that the smaller force must be applied over a longer distance to do the same task. The force-distance trade-off is the mechanical advantage of machines. There is an advantage to using a machine. The advantage is that you have to apply less force through a longer distance than without a machine.

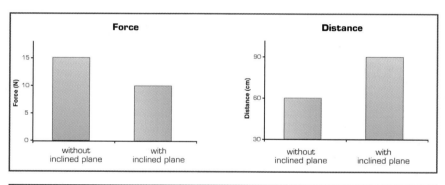

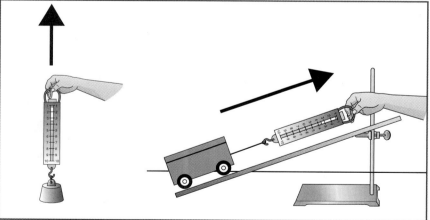

The mechanical advantage of a machine can be seen clearly in graphs that show the relationship between force and distance. The graphs shown are similar to the graphs that you created in class when you investigated the inclined plane. These two graphs show the results when a weight was moved from the floor to the top of a table that was 60 cm high. First it was lifted straight up. Then an inclined plane was used. The first graph compares the amount of force applied to move the weight. Without an inclined plane, 15 N of force were required to move the weight. Using an inclined plane, only 10 N of force were needed.

The advantage of using the inclined plane was that less force was needed to move the weight. What was the trade-off? Without the inclined plane, the force was applied through a distance of 60 cm. However, using the inclined plane to move the weight, the force was applied through 90 cm. The trade-off for using the inclined plane was that the force had to be applied through a longer distance.

How would you write a conclusion for this investigation? You would need to describe what the data show. In general, you found that less force was needed to move the weight when using an inclined plane than to lift it straight up. You also needed to apply the force through a longer distance when using an inclined plane. You might write a conclusion like the following: "When using an inclined plane to move a weight, less force is applied. However, the force is applied through a greater distance than when lifting the weight straight up."

You can use the data from the investigation as evidence to support the conclusion. What is the evidence to support the claim that when an inclined plane was used, *less force* was applied? The data show that when using the inclined plane a force of 10 N of force was applied. When lifting straight up, 15 N of force was applied. A force of 10 N is less than 15 N, so this evidence supports your claim.

Now look at the second part of the conclusion. The claim states that when the inclined plane was used, the force was applied through a *greater distance* than when you lifted the weight directly. What is the evidence to support this claim? In the data, when the inclined plane was used, the weight moved 90 cm. When lifting straight up, the weight moved only 60 cm. A distance of 90 cm is greater than 60 cm, so this evidence supports the claim that the distance was greater using the inclined plane.

Revise Your Explanation

Look at the explanations you have created so far for inclined planes. Work with your group to revise your explanation. When you revise an explanation, you should consider any new information you have. You just read an explanation about using an inclined plane. In the last section, you also read about other simple machines that are a variation of an inclined plane. Revise your explanation about using an inclined plane to include the screw and the wedge.

Make sure when you revise one part that the whole explanation still makes sense. If you think an additional claim and explanation is needed based on what you have just learned, spend time in your group working on that too. Use a new *Create Your Explanation* page for each explanation you develop.

Communicate

Share Your Explanation

When you are finished, share your new explanations with the class. Discuss each explanation to make sure it is clear and complete.

work: when a force acts on an object and the object moves a distance in the direction of the force, then work has been done.

machine: a device that helps you do work more easily with it than without it.

What is Work?

When a force acts on an object and the object moves a distance in the direction of the force, scientists say that **work** has been done. You did work when you lifted the weight straight up. You also did work when you pulled the weight up the inclined plane.

But you will probably be surprised to learn that when you pushed on the heavy bucket and it did not move, scientists would say that you did not do any work. You may have tried hard, but the bucket did not move. According to the scientific definition of work, it does not matter how hard you push or pull on an object. If the object does not move, no work has been done.

Work is being done.

no motion   no motion

No work is done.

Science definitions are often different and more exact than the way you use words in everyday conversation. Work is one of those words that has a different meaning scientifically than it has when you use it in everyday conversation. You might talk about "working hard on an assignment" or "working with others to get something done." In everyday terms, that means you tried hard and did things together. From a scientific point of view, there was only work being done if what you were doing was moving something from one place to another.

The inclined plane made it easier for you to do work. One function of a **machine** is to help you do work more easily. However, a machine does not change the *amount* of work that is done. It only changes the force that is required to do the work. You did the same amount of work to lift the weight straight up as you did to pull it to the same height up the ramp. You used less force to pull the weight up the ramp than you did to lift it straight up. However, you had to apply this lesser force over a greater distance. The amount of work done when a force is applied to move an object depends on two things:

- the amount of force needed
- the distance over which that force is applied

These are the two things that are traded off when using a machine.

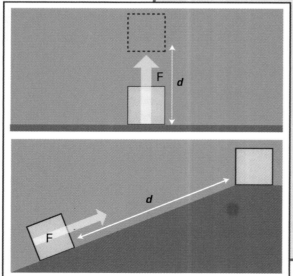

Reflect

It is winter and you have a "snow day." School is cancelled. You and your friends are building a snowman. You roll a huge snowball for the bottom, and another big snowball for the middle. As you and your friends try to add the head, you realize that the snowball is too heavy and the body of the snowman is too tall for you to lift the head to the top. You ask your friends, "Now what do we do?" Your best friend remembers something about machines he learned in science class that could save the day. What do you think he remembered?

You remember your work with machines in science class. How can you use the information about inclined planes to move the head to the top of the snowman? You find two boards to choose from, a long one and a short one. Draw a diagram that shows the board you choose and how you will use it to get the head of the snowman on the top of the snowman.

What's the Point?

Scientists are always trying to understand why things function the way they do. They make the best explanations they can as they investigate. But scientists are constantly learning more. They revise their explanations to make them more accurate and complete as they add to what they know. You had a chance to do the same thing.

You also read that work is done when a force acts on an object and the object moves for a distance in the direction of the force. A machine helps you do work more easily than you can without a machine. However, it does not change the amount of work you do. It only changes the force you need to apply to move an object.

Learning Set 2

Back to the Big Question

How do machines help move large, heavy objects?

You've raised questions about how machines work and learned about different types of machines. You then did investigations to find out how a machine affects force. You created and revised explanations summarizing the effects of a machine on force. However, your challenge for this Unit is to help the biologists, Drs. Enrique, Susan, and Tanika, lift a large crate to the top of a cliff. Remember, you are trying to answer the question *How do machines help move large, heavy objects?*

Plan Your Design

Get a drawing of the beach and cliff area from your teacher. Meet with your group and decide how Drs. Enrique, Susan, and Tanika might be able to use an inclined plane to help solve their problem. You will sketch where and how an inclined plane might be used on the drawing.

Also, think of ways in which you might use an inclined plane in your model of the cliff. Think about how you could attach and use the inclined plane to the box that represents the cliff.

Describe how the force and distance trade-off would apply to this problem. Try to estimate (make an educated guess) how much their applied force could be reduced by using this machine. For example, would the applied force be reduced by one-half or one-quarter? Be sure to explain your estimate using the information you learned during this *Learning Set*.

Communicate Your Idea

Plan Briefing

While you are coming up with a solution for the biologists, your teacher
might have you present your idea-in-progress to the class in a short *Plan
Briefing*. At this stage in the process, it is important for the briefing
to move quickly and have focus. Be prepared to present your idea and
rationale for using an inclined plane. Show your sketch to the rest of the
class. Explain to the class how this machine might be helpful and how it
helps you answer the *Big Question*.

Your group's experience may provide valuable lessons for others. If you are having trouble thinking of ideas and a solution, a *Plan Briefing* will give you a chance to get help.

Build Your Design

You have planned your design and seen the plans of others. Now it is time for you to construct the solution you have planned to test your current ideas. You will be using the same model as in *Learning Set 1.* Your materials will include the weight and the threads. Remember how many threads were needed to pull the weight up the cliff. Build your machine and see how many threads you need to lift the weights. When you are finished with your building, you will share your solution with the class.

Communicate

Solution Briefing

You have built your design and tested it. You had some ideas about how to use an inclined plane in your machine. But you may have found that your plan did not work out just the way you thought it would. By sharing your results with the class, everyone will be able to learn from your experiences.

As you prepare for your presentation, identify the two most important ideas you learned from building your design. Be prepared to describe the advantages and disadvantages of your design. In what situations might your design work well and in what situations might you have difficulty making your design work?

As you listen to other groups' ideas, identify what you are learning about mechanical advantage and its tradeoffs. What are you learning that will allow you to design a better solution to the challenge next time you have a chance?

Update the *Project Board*

The *What are we learning?* column on the *Project Board* helps you pull together everything you have learned. Remember to always include your evidence. You can then use what you have learned to answer the *Big Question* or address the challenge. Each investigation you do is like a piece of a puzzle. You must fit the pieces together to help you address the challenge.

Your *Big Question* was *How do machines help move large, heavy objects?* The last column, *What does it mean for the challenge or question?* is the place to write down how mechanical advantage, force-distance tradeoff, and the benefits of an inclined plane can help you answer the *Big Question*.

Learning Set 3

What Other Machines Can Change Force?

You have learned about three simple machines—the inclined plane, the wedge, and the screw. You learned that the wedge and the screw are actually variations of the inclined plane. Each of these simple machines can increase a force to make an object move. Machines allow people to move big things that they could not move on their own.

If you look around, you would be able to quickly find an example of each. There may be a flag in front of your school. Each day, the flag is raised and lowered using a pulley. At a playground, you are likely to see a seesaw. This simple board, balanced on a support in the middle, is an example of a lever. If you turn a doorknob to open a door, you are using a wheel and axle!

3.1 Understand the Question

Thinking about Other Machines That Can Change Force

The question for this *Learning Set* is *What other machines can change force?*. You know that an inclined plane, a wedge, and a screw reduce the force required to move an object. However, the trade-off is that you must apply this force over a longer distance. Other simple machines, such as the wedge, also change the direction of the force.

How can this information be used to help you design a machine that can lift a heavy crate up 20 m (65 ft) to the top of a cliff? What have you learned so far that can be helpful? Are there other machines such as the lever, pulley, and wheel and axle that may be possibilities?

Get Started

Below are some students' ideas about how to apply what they have learned so far to the problem. Read and think about each student's idea.

Michelle: "We know, for sure, that we must generate an unbalanced force that is strong enough to overcome the force of gravity."

Aiden: "An inclined plane seems like the most practical machine so far, but the distance is too far."

Jack: "I don't think we should try to change the direction of the force. I think we need something to reduce the amount of force needed."

Julie: "None of the machines we have learned about so far seem ideal. There has to be something else. Maybe, there are machines we can combine."

Conference

In your group, discuss whether you agree or disagree with each student? What might you say to each student? What might you investigate to determine if a student's idea is correct? After your conference, you will discuss your answers to these questions with your class.

Individually, develop two questions that might help you learn about other machines and how they help to move heavy objects. When you write your questions, keep in mind that your questions should

- be interesting to you,
- require several resources to answer,
- relate to the *Big Question* and the crate-lift problem, and
- require collecting and using data.

Remember to avoid yes/no questions and those that require only a one-sentence answer.

When you have completed your two questions, take the questions back to your small group. Share all the questions with each other. Carefully consider each question. Decide if it meets the criteria for a good question. With your group, refine the questions that do not meet the criteria. Choose the two most interesting questions to share with the class. Give your teacher the rest of the questions so they might be used later.

Update the *Project Board*

Return to the *Project Board* to update it. You can add any new questions or ideas you might have. For example, you may have had some experience with a lever, pulley, or wheel and axle and would like to suggest your ideas for the *Project Board*. Also post the two questions that your group developed in the *What do we need to investigate?* column.

Later in this *Learning Set*, you will conduct some investigations and use models to understand how some other machines can help make moving big things easier. The investigations will require you to make careful observations and record all your results. The *Project Board* can help you to organize what you are doing as you proceed.

3.2 Investigate

How Do Levers Change a Force?

Imagine that you are by yourself and you need to move a big rock. You try lifting and pushing the rock, but it will not move. However, you do see a long stick and a brick. Think about how you could use these to move the rock.

If you have ever used a stick to pry a rock out of a hole, you have used a **lever**. Levers are very basic machines. In their simplest form, they can be a **rigid** bar resting on a **pivot** point. This pivot point is called a **fulcrum**. The object that is being lifted is called the load. The push or pull on the lever is called the force. You can see each of these on the lever diagram. Just like all machines, levers can make doing work easier.

In this investigation, you will answer the question, *How do different levers help you move a weight?*.

Predict

In the next investigations, you are going to use a lever and see how it changes the force needed to lift an object. A lever is a simple machine. You know that simple machines reduce the force needed to lift something. But the trade-off is that the simple machine adds to the distance you need to lift an object.

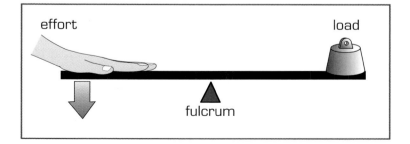

rigid: stiff.

lever: a simple machine made up of a rigid bar that pivots around a fixed point (called a fulcrum).

pivot: the point on which something rests and turns.

fulcrum: the point about which the rigid bar of a lever pivots.

History Connection

Levers, as well as inclined planes, were among the first tools to be used by early humans. The use of levers can be traced back to 5000 B.C.

Materials

- **spring scale (0 N–20 N)**
- **weight**
- **ring stand**
- **bolt (3 in)**
- **washers**
- **wing nut**
- **right-angle clamp**
- **wooden lever with eyehooks**
- **string**
- **scissors**
- **2 1-m rulers**

On a graph like those you used in the last *Learning Set*, sketch your prediction about what you think is going to happen when you lift the weight using a lever. You will explore use of three different levers. The fulcrum on each will be in a different place, starting at the center of the lever and moving closer to the load.

Procedure

In this investigation, you are going to use a lever to lift a weight. First, you will lift the weight straight up. Then you will lift it to the same height using various levers. The first lever will have the fulcrum located at the center of the board. For the next parts of the investigation, you will move the fulcrum closer to the load. You will compare the force applied and the distance moved.

Part 1: Lifting the Weight without a Lever

In this part of the investigation, you will be lifting the weight 10 cm from the top of the table. Use the ruler to measure the height accurately. Use the spring scale to measure how much force you had to use to lift the weight off the table.

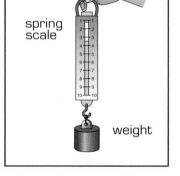

spring scale

weight

1. Use the diagram to help you set up your equipment correctly.
2. Attach the spring scale to the weight. Lift the weight 10 cm above the table using the spring scale. Measure the 10 cm from the top of the table to the bottom of the weight.
3. The amount of force you used to lift the weight is shown on the spring scale. Read the amount of force in newtons (N) you used to lift the weight. Record that measurement on your data table.
4. On the data table, record the distance the weight moved as 10 cm.
5. Repeat this procedure in the same way two more times for a total of three trials. Record all the data on your data table.

You have now lifted the weight to see how much force you need to lift the weight straight up from the table. This weight was not too heavy to lift. Some weights, like the crate on the beach, are very heavy. Use the next part of this procedure to see how a lever can help move the weight.

Part 2: Using a Lever to Lift the Weight

In this part of the investigation, you will be using a lever with the fulcrum in three different places to lift the weight 10 cm. The height you will lift the weight will stay constant so you will be able to compare your force data to the force data for just lifting the weight straight off the table. You will need to measure the distance you pulled to get the weight 10 cm from the table.

1. Use the diagram to help you set up your equipment correctly. Notice the parts that are identified: fulcrum, effort, and load. The lever should be in the horizontal position and the fulcrum is at the center. Put the meter stick next to the lever and measure 10 cm up from the table. Hold the ruler at this position.

2. Attach the spring scale to the lever at one end. Hang the weight from the other end of the lever.

3. Put the other meter stick next to your hand. Be ready to measure how far you have to pull down on the lever.

4. Pull down on the spring scale until the weight is 10 cm from the table.

5. The amount of force you used to lift the weight is shown on the spring scale. Read the amount of force in newtons (N) you used to lift the weight. Record that measurement on your data table.

6. Use the ruler to measure how far down your hand moved to pull the weight up 10 cm. On the data table, record the distance your hand moved.

7. Repeat this procedure in the same way two more times for a total of three trials. Record all the data on your data table.

8. Move the fulcrum of the lever toward the load. Set it in the next hole. Repeat *Steps 2* through *7* of the procedure.

9. Move the fulcrum one more hole closer to the load. Again, repeat *Steps 2* through *7*.

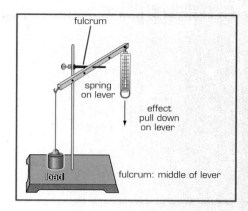

fulcrum: middle of lever

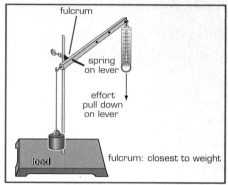

fulcrum: closest to weight

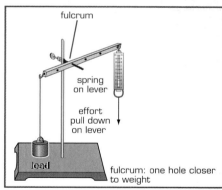

fulcrum: one hole closer to weight

Recording Your Data

Use the following tables to record your data from each trial.

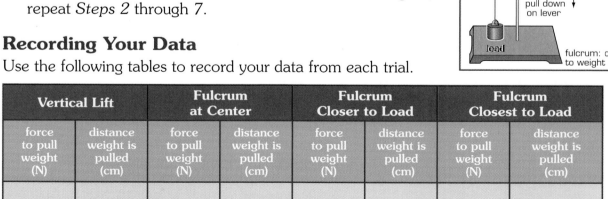

Vertical Lift		Fulcrum at Center		Fulcrum Closer to Load		Fulcrum Closest to Load	
force to pull weight (N)	distance weight is pulled (cm)	force to pull weight (N)	distance weight is pulled (cm)	force to pull weight (N)	distance weight is pulled (cm)	force to pull weight (N)	distance weight is pulled (cm)

Vertical lift		Fulcrum at center		Fulcrum closer to load		Fulcrum closest to load	
Average force to lift weight (N)	Average distance weight is lifted (cm)	Average force to pull weight (N)	Average distance weight is pulled (cm)	Average force to pull weight (N)	Average distance weight is pulled (cm)	Average force to pull weight (N)	Average distance weight is pulled (cm)

Analyze Your Data

You should now have data from lifting the weight straight from the table and then lifting the block the same height, 10 cm, with three different levers. You will now analyze your data to see how the levers made a difference in how much force was required to lift the block.

Force

You took three force measurements for each part of the investigation. Average these measurements to find the average force needed for each part. You should have four data points when you are finished.

Create a bar chart using these average measurements. Bar one should be the lift straight off the table, bar two is the horizontal lever, and so on. Make sure you have four bars on your chart when you are finished.

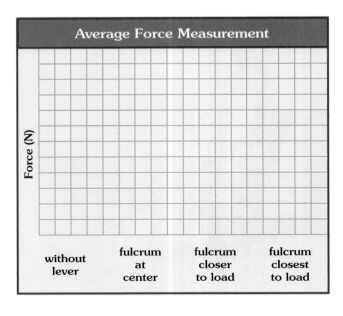

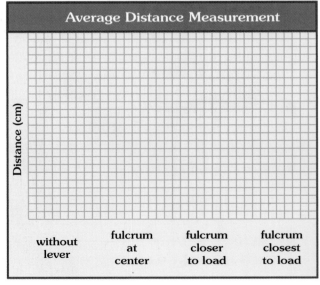

Distance

You took three distance measurements for each part of the investigation. The distance is how far you had to move your hand to pull the weight off the table 10 cm. Average the distance for each part. You should have four data points when you are finished.

Create another bar chart using these average measurements. Bar one should be the lift straight off the table, bar two is the horizontal lever, and so on. Make sure you have four data points on your graph when you are finished.

The two bar charts you have created give you a lot of information about the relationship between force and distance when you use a lever to help you lift something. Answer the following questions to help you better understand the charts.

1. The force bar chart shows the trend in the data for force. As you moved the fulcrum toward the load, what happened to the amount of force needed to lift the weight 10 cm off the table? Start your claim with, "As the fulcrum is moved toward the load, ..." Use evidence and science knowledge to support your claim.

2. The distance bar chart shows the trend in the data for distance. As you move the fulcrum toward the load, what happens to the distance you move your hand in order to lift the weight 10 cm off the table? Start your claim with, "As the fulcrum is moved toward the load, ..." Use evidence and science knowledge to support your claim.

3. The two bar charts work together to help you better understand another aspect of machines. Observe the trends on both charts. Explain the relationship between force and distance from these charts. Start your claim with "As the fulcrum moves toward the load, the force ... and the distance ..." Make sure to include both force and distance in your sentence. Use evidence and science knowledge to support your claim.

Communicate Your Results

Investigation Expo

Scientists always share their understandings with each other. Presenting their results is one of the most important things scientists do. You will share what you have found in an *Investigation Expo*. To prepare for this, you will make a poster that answers the following questions:

- What question were you trying to answer in the investigation?

- What procedure did you use and do you feel it was a fair test?

- What materials did you use?

- What is your interpretation of the results and how confident are you in them?

The handle of this old-fashioned water pump is an example of a first-class lever.

Remember, it is important to report the procedure you used in your investigation. Each group may run their investigations differently. It will be important to compare results from these different tests. If you think the test you ran was not as fair as you had planned, you might want to report on how you would change your procedure if you had the chance to run the investigation again.

Because everyone did the same investigation, during this *Investigation Expo* you will put your posters on the wall. When all the posters are displayed, you and your classmates can walk around and look at each one.

As you look at the other posters, examine them closely to see if you can answer this set of questions for each one.

- What was the group trying to find out?

- What variables did they control as they did their procedure?

- Is their data scattered or is it fairly consistent?

- Did they measure the force required to lift the weight in a consistent way each time the fulcrum was moved?

- Did their procedure cause them to run a poor, uncontrolled experiment?

- What did they learn?

- What conclusions do their results suggest?

- Are their results the same as yours? If not, why not?

After looking at the posters, your class will discuss the answers to these questions and what you learned from your investigations about levers and how they help lift heavy things.

Reflect

As you answer the following questions, reflect on the lever investigations you just completed. Also, think about how the lever is similar to the inclined plane. Be prepared to share your answers with the class.

1. What happened to the amount of force needed to lift the weight as the fulcrum was moved closer to the weight?

2. What happened to the distance you had to move the lever down as the fulcrum was moved closer to the weight?

3. In the last section, you learned about mechanical advantage. All machines have some mechanical advantage. Describe the mechanical advantage of the levers you investigated.

What's the Point?

In this section, you investigated levers and how the position of the fulcrum affects the amount of force needed to lift a weight. You also compared distances through which the force was applied in each situation. The bar charts helped you understand the relationship between force and distance for the levers. They showed that the amount of force needed to lift the weight decreased as the fulcrum moved closer to the load. The trade-off of force and distance is common to all simple machines. When the fulcrum is moved closer to the load, less force is needed to move the block but you have to move the lever a greater distance.

In an oil pump, a lever is used to create a suction that draws oil up from the ground.

MOVING BIG THINGS

3.3 Explain

Create an Explanation for How a Lever Changes a Force

The purpose of a science explanation is to help others understand what was learned from a set of investigations and how the scientist reached this conclusion.

Later, other scientists will use these explanations to help them explain other phenomena and predict what will happen in other situations.

You will do the same thing now. Your claim will be the trend you found in your lever investigation. You will use data you collected and previous science knowledge you have to create a good explanation. It should describe how the applied force changes as the fulcrum is moved closer to the weight. You should also describe the relationship between the applied force and the distance the lever must be moved.

Because your understanding of the science of forces and levers is not complete, you may not be able to write a full explanation. Do your best based on what you understand now. As you learn more, you can make your explanation better.

Explain

Recall that an explanation is made up of three parts:

- Claim – a statement of what you understand or a conclusion that you have reached from an investigation or set of investigations

- Evidence – data collected during investigations and trends in that data

- Science knowledge – knowledge about how things work. You may have learned this through reading, talking to an expert, discussion, or other experiences.

An explanation is a statement that connects the claim to the evidence and science knowledge in a logical way. A good explanation will convince somebody that the claim is valid.

Do your best to explain the results of your investigation. Meet with your group to write an explanation of what happens to the force that must be applied as the fulcrum is moved closer to the weight. The *Create Your Explanation* page provides hints so that you will remember how to put an explanation together.

Communicate

Share Your Explanation

When everyone is finished, you will share your explanations with the class. Listen to the explanations made by other groups.

Use this information to come up with a class explanation. You will have an opportunity to revise your explanation after you learn more about levers.

Create Your Explanation
Name:_____ Date:_____
Use this page to explain the lesson of your recent investigations.
Write a brief summary of the results from your investigation. You will use this summary to help you write your Explanation.
Claim – a statement of what you understand or a conclusion that you have reached from an investigation or a set of investigations.
Evidence – data collected during investigations and trends in that data.
Science knowledge – knowledge about how things work. You may have learned this through reading, talking to an expert, discussion, or other experiences.
Write your Explanation using the *Claim*, *Evidence* and *Science knowledge*.

What's the Point?

Your class has completed an investigation of how a lever can affect how much force needs to be applied to move something. You now know how levers help to reduce the force you need to apply to move a weight. You also noticed that the distance you had to move the weight changed when the fulcrum was moved closer to the weight. Your explanation was a first attempt at describing the relationship between the force that had to be applied and the distance the weight had to be moved.

3.4 Investigate

How Do Pulleys Change a Force?

A mechanic may use pulleys to remove an old engine from a car.

A **pulley** is another example of a simple machine. It is made of a wheel and something to pull on, such as a rope or chain, laid over the wheel. When the rope moves, the wheel turns. A pulley can make lifting something much easier.

Pulleys are very important simple machines. They are used often. They may be used to move light things such as flags or window blinds. They are also used to move heavy things such as boats or elevator cars.

In this investigation, you will answer the question *How do different arrangements of pulleys help you move a weight?*.

Predict

Before you start your investigations, think about the other simple machines you have used to lift a weight. Sketch a flagpole pulley system. You can do this from memory or find a flag pole to copy. Then predict and mark the forces in the flagpole pulley system. Use force arrows to show the direction and size of each force.

pulley: a simple machine made up of a wheel with a groove that holds a rope.

fixed pulley: a pulley in which the shaft that the wheel rotates around (axle) does not move.

free pulley: a pulley in which the shaft that the wheel rotates around (axle) can move.

Procedure

Just as before, you will begin by raising the weight from the table, straight up. This is the control so you know how much force is required to lift the block without using a simple machine. Then you will lift the weight to the same height using a variety of pulleys. You will measure the force required when you use a **fixed pulley**, a **free pulley**, and a machine that combines a fixed and free pulley.

Part 1: Lifting the Weight without a Pulley

1. Use the diagram to help you set up your equipment correctly.

2. Attach the spring scale to the weight. Lift the weight 20 cm above the table using the spring scale. Measure 20 cm from the top of the table to the bottom of the weight.

3. The amount of force you used to lift the weight is shown on the spring scale. Read the amount of force in newtons (N) you used to lift the weight. Record that measurement on your data table.

4. On the data table, record the distance the weight moved as 20 cm.

5. Repeat this procedure in the same way two more times for a total of three trials. Record all the data on your data table.

Part 2: Using a Fixed Pulley to Lift the Weight

In this part of the investigation, you will use a fixed pulley to lift the weight 20 cm. The height you lift the weight will stay constant so you will be able to compare your force data to the force data for just lifting the block straight off the table. You will need to measure the distance you pulled to lift the weight 20 cm from the table.

1. Use the diagram to help you set up your equipment correctly. The pulley is fixed to the top of the stand and the string is over the top of the pulley. Put one meter stick next to the weight and measure 20 cm from the table. Hold the meter stick in this position.

2. Attach the spring scale to the string. Hang the weight from the other end of the string.

3. Put the other meter stick next to your hand. Be ready to measure how far you have to pull down on the string when the weight is raised 20 cm.

4. Pull down on the spring scale until the weight is 20 cm from the table.

5. The amount of force you used to lift the weight is shown on the spring scale. Read the amount of force in newtons (N) you used to lift the block. Record that measurement on your data table.

6. Use the ruler to measure how far up your hand moved to pull the weight up 20 cm. On the data table, record the distance your hand moved.

Materials

- spring scale (0 N–20 N)
- weight
- 2 pulleys
- string
- ruler
- ring stand
- scissors
- right-angle clamp
- screw
- 2 washers
- bolt (3 in.)
- wingnut

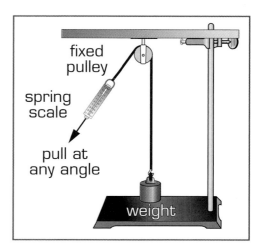

fixed pulley

spring scale

pull at any angle

weight

7. Repeat this procedure in the same way two more times for a total of three trials. Record all the data on your data table.

Part 3: Using a Free Pulley to Lift the Weight

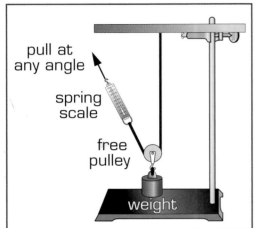

pull at any angle

spring scale

free pulley

weight

In this part of the investigation, you will use a free pulley to lift the weight 20 cm. The height you lift the block will stay constant. You will need to measure the distance you pulled to lift the weight 20 cm off the table.

1. Use the diagram to help you set up your equipment correctly. The pulley is able to move and the string is looped under the pulley. Put one meter stick next to the weight and measure 20 cm from the table. Hold the meter stick in this position.

2. Attach the spring scale to the string. Attach the weight from the other end of the string.

3. Put the other meter stick next to your hand, be ready to measure how far you have to pull up on the string to raise the weight 20 cm.

4. Pull up on the spring scale until the weight is 20 cm from the table.

5. The amount of force you used to lift the weight is shown on the spring scale. Read the amount of force you used to lift the weight. Record that measurement on your data table.

6. Use the ruler to measure how far up your hand moved to pull the weight up 20 cm. On the data table, record the distance your hand moved.

Repeat this procedure in the same way two more times for a total of three trials. Record all the data on your data table.

Recording your Data

Use a table like the one below to organize your data.

Vertical lift		With fixed pulley		With free pulley		With fixed and free pully	
Force to lift weight (N)	Distance weight is lifted (cm)	Force to pull weight (N)	Distance weight is pulled (cm)	Force to pull weight (N)	Distance weight is pulled (cm)	Force to pull weight (N)	Distance weight is pulled (cm)

Vertical Lift		With Fixed Pulley		With Free Pulley		With Fixed and Free Pulley	
average force to pull weight (N)	average distance weight is pulled (cm)	average force to pull weight (N)	average distance weight is pulled (cm)	average force to pull weight (N)	average distance weight is pulled (cm)	average force to pull weight (N)	average distance weight is pulled (cm)

Analyze Your Data

You should now have data from lifting the weight straight from the table and then lifting it to the same height with two different pulleys. You will now analyze your data to see how the pulleys changed the size and direction of the force.

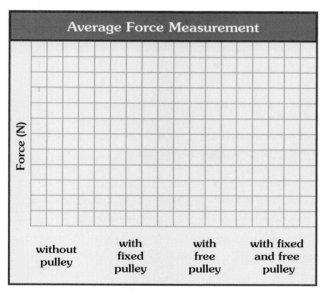

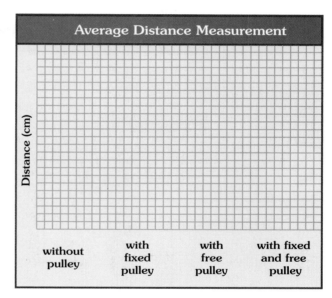

Force

Calculate the average force measurements for each part of the investigation. Create a bar chart using the average measurements for force. Bar one should be the lift straight off the table, bar two is the fixed pulley, and bar three is the free pulley. Make sure you have three bars on your chart when you are finished.

Distance

Calculate the average distance measurements for each part of the investigation. Create a bar chart using the average measurements for distance. Bar one should be the lift straight off the table, bar two is the fixed pulley, and bar three is the free pulley. Make sure you have three bars on your chart when you are finished.

Stop and Think

1. You have used two different types of pulleys to lift the same weight and they worked differently. Compare the two different pulleys. Explain how the forces changed when you used each pulley. Describe how the direction of the pull compared with the direction of the movement for each pulley.

2. Describe two situations in which you might want to use a fixed pulley and two situations in which you might want to use a free pulley.

Predict

You are now going to combine the fixed and free pulleys to see what happens when you use these two pulleys together. This is the first time you will use more than one simple machine to move the weight. Predict how you think the force and direction will be different when you use the two machines in combination. Record your prediction.

Procedure

Part 4: Combining a Fixed and Free Pulley to Lift the Weight

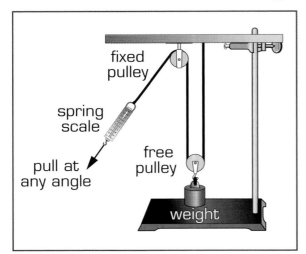

In this part of the investigation, you will use both a fixed and free pulley to lift the weight 20 cm. You will measure the force required to lift it 20 cm. You will also measure the distance you pulled to get the weight 20 cm off the table.

1. Use the diagram to help you set up your equipment correctly. The fixed pulley will hang from the top of the stand. The free pulley will move with the string.

2. Loop the string over the fixed pulley and under the free pulley. Make sure both ends of the string are free. Attach a spring scale to one end and the weight to the other end.

3. Put one of the meter sticks next to the weight and measure 20 cm from the table. Hold the meter stick in this position.

4. Put the other meter stick next to your hand. Be ready to measure how far you have to pull up on the string top raise the weight 20 cm.

5. Pull up on the spring scale until the weight is 20 cm from the table.

6. The amount of force you used to lift the weight is shown on the spring scale. Read the amount of force in newtons (N) you used to lift the block. Record that measurement on your data table.

7. Use the ruler to measure how far up your hand moved to pull the weight up 20 cm. On the data table, record the distance your hand moved.

8. Repeat this procedure in the same way two more times for a total of three trials. Record all the data on your data table.

Recording your Data

Record your data for this part of the investigation in your pulley table.

Analyze your Data

The fixed and free pulleys change force differently. Add the data for this part of the investigation to the bar charts you created earlier. Answer these questions.

1. How was the force and distance different this time?

2. How did the actual results compare to your prediction?

3. How accurately did you predict the final results?

4. What is the advantage of a pulley system that includes both a free and a fixed pulley?

A sailboat uses many different pulley systems.

Communicate Your Results

Investigation Expo

When you are finished with your investigation, you will share your results with the class during an *Investigation Expo*. During an *Investigation Expo*, your group will present the procedure you followed, the data you obtained, and the meaning of your results. An investigation poster is one way to help you present and explain this information. As you are presenting to your classmates, they will want to understand

- What question were you trying to answer in the investigation?
- What procedure did you use and do you feel it was a fair test?
- What materials did you use?
- What is your interpretation of the results and how confident are you in them?

Make a poster that includes all five items listed above. Present them in a way that will make it easy for someone to look at your poster and identify what you have done and what you found out. If you think the test you ran was not as fair as you had planned, your poster should also have a report on how you would change your procedure if you had the chance to run the experiment again.

Look for differences in how groups completed the investigation. Make sure the data seems consistent from one group to another. Be sure to point out any errors you see in procedure, variable control, or interpretation of the data.

As others present their work, look for answers to these questions:

- What was the group trying to find out?
- What variables did they control as they did their procedure?
- Is their data scattered or is it fairly consistent?
- Did they measure the force needed to lift the weight in a consistent way?
- Did their procedure cause them to run a poor, uncontrolled experiment?
- What did they learn?
- What conclusions do their results suggest?

Ask questions that you need answered to understand results and to satisfy yourself that the results and conclusions others have drawn are true. Be sure that you trust the results that other groups report.

Explain

You have written explanations of how two simple machines, the inclined plane and the lever, change the force required to move a weight. You just investigated a third type of simple machine, the pulley. Write an explanation of how pulleys can change force.

Recall that an explanation is made up of three parts:

- Claim—a statement of what you understand or a conclusion that you have reached from an investigation or set of investigations
- Evidence—data collected during investigations and trends in that data
- Science knowledge—knowledge about how things work. You may have learned this through reading, talking to an expert, discussion, or other experiences.

Do your best to explain the results of your investigation. Meet with your group to write an explanation of what happens to the force that must be applied as the fulcrum is moved closer to the weight. The *Create Your Explanation* page provides hints so that you'll remember how to put an explanation together.

Communicate

Share Your Explanation

When everyone is finished, you will share your explanations with the class. Record the explanations made by other groups. You might also create a poster for the classroom that has the full set of explanations on it. You will have an opportunity to revise your explanations after you learn more about levers.

What's the Point?

Different types of pulleys make moving things easier in different ways. You found that the fixed pulley did not change the amount of force needed to lift the weight. However, it changed the direction in which the force was applied. The moveable pulley reduced the force required, but did not change the direction of the force. When these different types of pulleys are combined into a system, you get the benefits of each type.

Cable and pulley arrangement used alongside railroad tracks.

3.5 Read

How Do a Pulley, a Lever, and a Wheel and Axle Change Force?

You just investigated two more simple machines, the lever and the pulley. In the investigations, you were able to see that simple machines can do two things. They can change the direction of the force or they can multiply the force. In this section, you will learn more about the lever and pulley. You will also read about one other type of simple machine, the wheel and axle.

In a seesaw, the fulcrum is halfway between the load and the effort.

The Lever

You may have played on a seesaw (teeter-totter) at the playground. A seesaw is so much fun because your friend's weight pushing down lifts you up. A seesaw is an example of a lever. A seesaw can be used to lift heavy objects. In the investigation, you use a lever to lift a weight.

All levers have some type of pivot point called a fulcrum. The lever rotates, or turns, around the fulcrum. The position of the fulcrum when compared to where the force, or effort, is applied, determines how the lever can be used. The applied force is called the **effort**. The weight being moved is called the **load**. Differences in the position of the fulcrum, the effort, and the load result in three different classes of levers.

Scissors, boat oars, and crowbars are all similar levers. When you push on one end of the lever, the other end of the lever pushes up. These are all **first-class levers** because the fulcrum is between the effort and the load. First class levers can change the direction of the effort.

effort: the applied force.

load: the weight being moved or the resisting force.

first-class lever: a lever in which the fulcrum is positioned between the effort (applied force) and the load (weight being moved).

Scissors are made up of two first-class levers connected by a pivot point. The pivot point acts as a fulcrum. When you push down on the top handle of a pair of scissors, that blade moves up. As you lift up on the bottom handle of the scissors, that blade moves down.

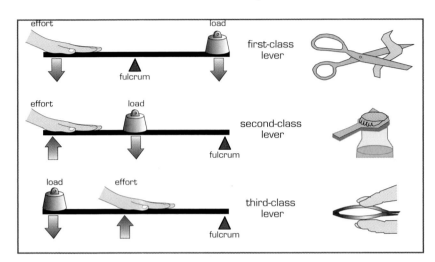

First-class levers can also multiply the applied force. If the fulcrum of a first-class lever is moved closer to the weight being moved (the load) the amount of force (effort) needed to move the load is less. However, the effort end of the lever, where the force is being applied, must move a greater distance than the load.

For example, branch cutters are designed to cut through much thicker, tougher materials than scissors. Look at the pictures of the scissors and branch cutters. Notice the difference between them. The fulcrum (pivot point) is closer to the load end in the branch cutters. The load end, or blades, of the branch cutters is much shorter than the effort end, or the handles. The blades move a smaller distance than the handles. This is because the force, or effort, is being applied through a longer distance. The tradeoff is that it takes less force to cut through thick branches, but you must apply the force over a greater distance.

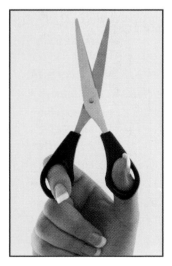

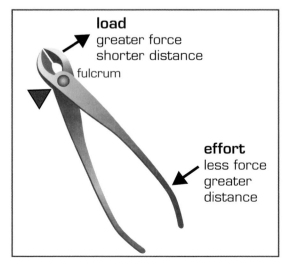

In **second-class levers**, the load is positioned between the fulcrum and the applied force, or effort. Second-class levers do not change the direction of the force. However, they do multiply the applied force. A bottle opener is a good example. As you lift on the end of the bottle opener, it lifts the cap off the bottle. A nutcracker is another example of a second-class lever. You apply a force at the end of the handles to crack a nut between them.

Third-class levers have the fulcrum positioned at one end and the load at the other end. The force is applied in the middle. Like second-class levers, third-class levers do not change the direction of the force. Third-class levers multiply the distance of the applied force. This means that the force you apply must always be greater than the force of the load.

Tweezers are a good example of a third-class lever. You squeeze the tweezers in the middle and they exert a force at the end. A broom is another example of a third-class lever. The fulcrum is at the top of the broom, you apply a force in the middle, and the broom moves dirt at the bottom. In both examples, the amount of force you apply is greater than the force needed to do the task. However, the distance you must apply the force is much less. It is easier in these cases to apply more force through a short distance than to apply less force through a long distance.

second-class lever: a lever in which the load is positioned between the fulcrum and the applied force.

third-class lever: a lever in which the effort is positioned between the fulcrum and the load.

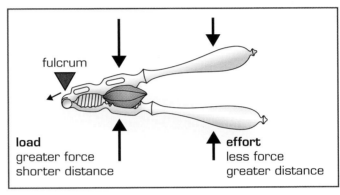

fulcrum

load
greater force
shorter distance

effort
less force
greater distance

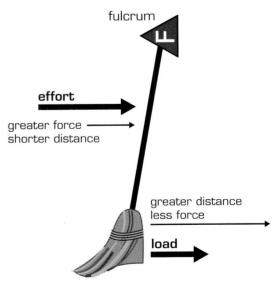

fulcrum

effort

greater force
shorter distance

greater distance
less force

load

The Pulley

The pulley is another type of simple machine. As you saw in your investigation, there are two types of pulleys—the fixed pulley and the free pulley. Fixed pulleys are attached to a fixed support, like a wall or ceiling. A fixed pulley changes the direction of the applied force. For example, it can change a pulling force into a lifting force. Fixed pulleys do not reduce the amount of force you need to apply.

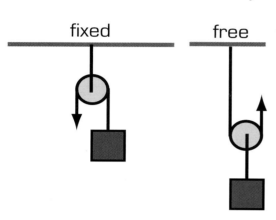

A free pulley is attached to the load. The pulley moves along with the load when the string is pulled. A free pulley reduces the amount of force needed to move the weight, but does not change the direction of the force.

Fixed pulleys and free pulleys can be combined to make a pulley system. You then get the benefit of each type. In a pulley system, you must pull on more rope than if you were just lifting the load. The system, however, changes the pulling force to a lifting force and reduces the amount of force needed to lift the load. You may have seen a pulley being used on a sailboat to lift the sails or on a weightlifting machine at the gym.

The Wheel and Axle

wheel and axle: a simple machine made up of a wheel (a circular object) that turns around an axle (a circular object that is smaller than the wheel).

The final type of simple machine is the **wheel and axle**. The wheel and axle changes a small force into a larger force. The small force is applied in a turning direction to the wheel. This changed into a larger turning force, applied at the center of the wheel (axle). An example of a wheel and axle is a steering wheel in a car. The force that a driver applies to the outside edge of the steering wheel is much smaller than the force needed to turn the axle, which turns the car wheels. However, the edge of the steering wheel must move through a much longer distance than the axle. It has to move the whole distance around the outside of the steering wheel

Like other kinds of simple machines, a wheel and axle system makes it easier to do work. Also like other machines, there is a tradeoff between the amount of force you apply and the distance over which you must apply that force. Machines cannot change the amount of work that is done. They can only change the force that is required.

Stop and Think

1. Levers are used to lift very heavy things. The head of a claw hammer is one type of lever. Look at this picture of a claw hammer removing a nail. Identify the effort, load, and fulcrum of this lever. Identify the class of lever.

2. A mechanic's garage might have a pulley hanging from the ceiling. It might be used to lift an engine out of a car. Sketch a picture of how the pulley system might work.

3. A combination of pulleys has some advantages over using only one type of pulley. Explain one advantage of using combinations of pulleys.

3.6 Revise Your Explanation

How Do a Lever and a Pulley Change Force?

Explain

Look at the explanations you have created so far as a class. Work with your group to make your explanations better. When you revise an explanation, you should consider any new information you have, especially science information. Other times you will want to add new evidence or even revise the claim. It is important that all the parts of your explanation work together with each other. Make sure when you revise one part that the whole explanation still makes sense.

If you think an additional claim and explanation is needed based on what you have just learned, spend time in your group working on that, too. Use a new *Create Your Explanation* page for each explanation you create.

When you are finished, you'll share your revised explanations with the class and discuss the wording, so make sure it is clear and complete.

What's the Point?

From the investigations you did with levers and pulleys, you learned simple machines can do two things. They can either change the direction of the force or multiply the applied force. First-class levers and fixed pulleys both change the direction of the force. Second-class levers and free pulleys do not change the direction of the force. They both multiply the applied force. Third-class levers actually produce a force that is less than the applied force. However, they multiply the distance of the applied force.

One thing you have learned about all simple machines is that there is a tradeoff. A machine can multiply the applied force, but the tradeoff is that you must apply the force over a longer distance. No machine can increase the applied force and decrease the distance at the same time. A machine cannot change the amount of work required to move an object.

You may have seen this in the graphs you made from the data you collected during the investigations. For example, if a machine reduces the amount of force needed to move a weight then the distance must be increased. How much the applied force, or effort, is multiplied is the machine's mechanical advantage.

Learning Set 3

Back to the Big Question

How do machines help move large, heavy objects?

You have learned about levers and pulleys. You did investigations to find out how they affect the force required to move a weight. You created and revised explanations summarizing the effects of these machines on force. However, your challenge for this Unit is to help the biologists, Drs. Enrique, Susan, and Tanika, lift a large crate to the top of a cliff. Remember, you are trying to answer the question *How do machines help move large, heavy objects?*

Plan Your Design

Get a drawing of the beach and cliff area from your teacher. Meet with your group and decide how Drs. Enrique, Susan, and Tanika might be able to use a lever or pulleys to help solve their problem. You will sketch where and how these machines might be used on the drawing.

Also, think of ways in which you might use a lever or pulleys in your model of the cliff. Think about how you could attach them and use them with the box that represents the cliff.

Describe how the force and distance trade-off would apply to this problem. Try to estimate (make an educated guess) how much their applied force could be reduced by using each machine. For example, would the applied force be reduced by one-half or one-quarter? Be sure to explain your estimate using the information you learned during this *Learning Set*.

Communicate Your Ideas

Plan Briefing

While you are coming up with a solution for the biologists, your teacher might have you present your idea-in-progress to the class in a short *Plan Briefing*. At this stage in the process, it is important for the briefing to move quickly and have more focus. If your teacher calls for a *Plan Briefing*, be prepared to present your idea and rationale for using an inclined plane. Show your sketch to the rest of the class. Explain to the class how these machines might be helpful and how they help you answer the big question. Your group's experience may provide valuable lessons for others. If you are having trouble thinking of ideas and a solution, a *Plan Briefing* will give you a chance to get help.

Build Your Design

You have planned your design and seen the plans of others. Now it is time for you to construct the solution you have planned to test your current ideas. You will be using the same model as before. Your materials will include the weight and the threads. Remember how many threads were needed to pull the weight up the cliff. Build your new machine and see how many threads you need to lift the weight using a lever, pulley, or wheel and axle. When you are finished building, you will share your solution with the class.

Communicate

Solution Briefing

You have built your design and tested it. You had some ideas about how to use a lever, a pulley or a wheel and axle in your machine. But you may have found that your plan did not work out just the way you thought it would. By sharing your results with the class, everyone will be able to learn from your experiences.

As you prepare for your presentation, identify the two most important ideas you learned from building your design. Be prepared to describe the advantages and disadvantages of your design. In what situations might your design work well and in what situations might you have difficulty making your design work? As you listen to other groups' ideas, identify what you are learning about mechanical advantage and its tradeoffs. What are you learning that will allow you to design a better solution to the challenge next time you have a chance?

Update the *Project Board*

The *What have we learned?* column on the *Project Board* helps you pull together everything you have learned. Remember to always include your evidence. You can then use what you have learned to address the challenge and to answer the big question. Each investigation you do is like a piece of a puzzle. You must fit the pieces together to help you address the challenge. Your big question was *How do machines help move large, heavy objects?*. The last column, *What does it mean for the challenge or question?* is the place to write down how levers, pulleys, and wheels and axles can help you answer the big question.

Learning Set 4

How Can You Combine Simple Machines?

The *Big Question* for the Unit is *How do machines help move large, heavy objects?*. You learned about the forces that make objects move. You know that to change the speed or direction of an object, forces must be unbalanced. If the forces are equal, or balanced, then the object's motion will not change. Often, human strength by itself is not enough to generate an unbalanced force. You need to use a machine. The mechanical advantage of a machine describes how much a specific machine can multiply the force applied by the person operating it. Machines can also change the direction or distance of an applied force. A machine, however, cannot change the amount of work required to move an object.

complex machine: a machine that is a combination of two or more simple machines.

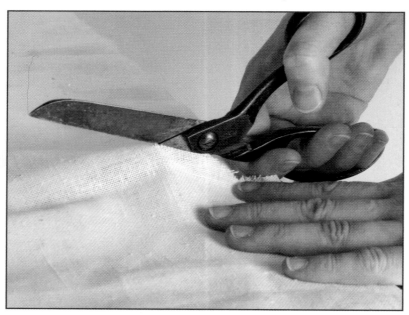

Scissors are made up of two first-class levers joined together at the fulcrum. The cutting edges are wedges.

You learned about six simple machines—the inclined plane, the wedge, the screw, the lever, the pulley, and the wheel and axle. A single simple machine cannot always provide enough mechanical advantage to perform a given task. In fact, very few of the machines you use everyday are simple machines. Most machines are made up of at least two, and often many more, simple machines. Machines that are made up of two or more simple machines working together are called **complex machines**.

4.1 Understand the Question

Thinking about How Simple Machines Can Be Combined

At the beginning of this Unit you observed many different machines at a construction site. Most of the machines were complex machines. The question for this *Learning Set* is *How can you combine simple machines?*. You saw that when you put two pulleys together, you got the benefits of both. For example, if you combine a fixed pulley and a free pulley, your machine would multiply the applied force and change the direction of the force. By increasing the number of wheels and ropes in a pulley system, you can increase the mechanical advantage. What do you think would happen if you combined other simple machines?

Get Started

In earlier investigations, you measured the force needed to pull a weight up an inclined plane. The results showed that there is an advantage to using this simple machine instead of lifting the weight straight up. You also investigated the amount of force needed to lift a weight using pulleys. Again, the results showed that less force was needed to lift the weight using a pulley. What do you think would happen if you were to combine an inclined plane and a pulley?

Procedure:

Part 1: Lifting a Weight Vertically, Using an Inclined Plane, and Using a Pulley

In this investigation, you are going to compare the force needed to lift a weight vertically, lift the weight with an inclined plane, and lift the weight with a pulley.

1. Lift the weight vertically with the spring scale as you have done in the other investigations. Read the amount of force you used to lift the weight. Record that measurement on your data table.

2. Use the less-steep inclined plane as you did in *Learning Set 2*

3. Put the weight in a cart at the bottom of the inclined plane. Using the spring scale, pull the weight and cart up until it reaches a vertical height of 20 cm. Record the force needed to lift the weight.

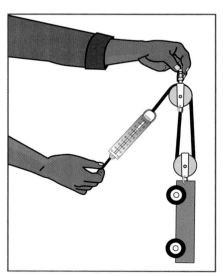

4. Set up a pulley system, using a fixed and a free pulley, as you did in the investigation with two pulleys in *Learning Set 3*. Instead of attaching the pulley to the ring stand, you can have one person in your group hold it up. Lift the weight 20 cm by pulling the string with the spring scale. Record the force needed to lift the weight with the two pulleys.

Stop and Think

1. What was the difference in the amount of force needed to lift the weight straight up and the amount of force needed to lift it using the inclined plane?

2. What is the mechanical advantage of the inclined plane?

3. What was the difference in the amount of forced needed to lift the weight straight up and the amount of force needed to lift it using the pulleys?

4. What is the mechanical advantage of the pulley system?

Predict

What do you think will happen to the mechanical advantage if you combine an inclined plane with a pulley system to lift the weight? Will the mechanical advantage be greater than if you used each simple machine alone? Write a prediction stating what you think will happen if you combine the inclined plane with the pulley system.

Procedure

Part 2: Lifting a Weight Using Both an Inclined Plane and a Pulley

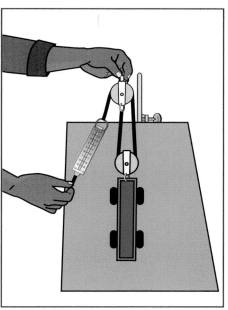

1. Have one person in your group hold the pulley at the top of the inclined plane. The weight in the cart should still be attached to the free pulley.

2. Place the weight and cart at the bottom of inclined plane. Attach the spring scale to the free end of the string that has been threaded through the pulley.

3. Pull the weight and cart up the ramp with the spring scale. Raise it to 20 cm above the table.

4. Measure the amount of force needed to lift the weight. Repeat three times and average the force measurements.

Stop and Think

1. What change did you observe in the force needed to raise the weight when you combined the inclined plane and the pulley system?

2. How did the mechanical advantage of the combined simple machines compare to using each simple machine alone?

Update the *Project Board*

You have just learned that simple machines can be combined to make complex machines. This idea might have a big effect on the machine you are designing to lift the crate from the beach to the top of the cliff. At this time, you probably have lots of ideas. You probably also have some questions about how this works. You should now work with your class to add to the *What are we learning?* column of the *Project Board*. Remember to include your understanding of mechanical advantage in simple machines and combinations of simple machines. Use evidence from your investigations to support what you have learned.

4.2 Read

How Do Simple Machines Work Together?

Think about some of the machines you have seen. You have looked at big machines such as cranes and backhoes. You have also examined pictures of handheld machines such as drills and screwdrivers. You have learned that some of the things you use everyday, such as scissors and pencil sharpeners are also machines. Sometimes it is easy to see that a machine is made up of different simple machines. At other times, it is not so easy. The photographs show complex machines. Each one is made up of two or more simple machines.

As you can see in these examples, in a complex machine two or more simple machines work together. The arm of a backhoe is actually a lever and a wedge that work together to get the job done. A wheel and axle and a wedge, working together, make up a screwdriver.

Crane

Backhoe

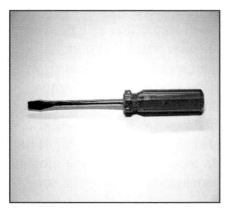
Screwdriver

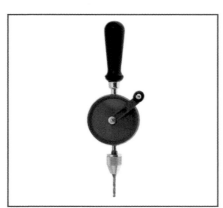
Drill

Pencil sharpener

Some machines, such as a pocketknife or multi-purpose tool, look like complex machines, but they are not. They are made of several different simple machines, but the simple machines are each used separately. For example, you would use the file on a pocketknife at a different time than you would use the knife blade. These two simple machines do not work together so the pocketknife is not a complex machine.

A shovel is an easy machine to use. It does not have any wheels, knobs, or other moving parts. It seems pretty simple. However, a shovel is a complex machine. It is made of two simple machines working together.

One simple machine that makes up a shovel is a lever. When lifting dirt out of the ground, the handle of a shovel acts as a lever. As you push down on the handle, the bottom of the lever lifts the dirt up. The fulcrum is located at the point where the shovel pivots in the dirt. In this way, the handle changes the direction of the applied force.

You apply less force to the shovel than you would to pull the dirt it is lifting out of the ground. However, your hands move down a larger distance than the dirt moves up. You are applying the force though a greater distance. The mechanical advantage of using the handle of a shovel is that you need to apply less force. Also, the handle changes the direction of the force. The tradeoff is that you need to apply the force through a greater distance.

A shovel would not be a good machine for digging if it only had a handle. In order for a shovel to help you dig up dirt, it also needs a second simple machine. The second simple machine on a shovel is a wedge. The bottom of the shovel scoop is shaped like a wedge. The wedge helps to push the scoop into the ground, so it can go under the dirt that you want to lift up. When you apply a downward force to the scoop, it pushes down on the top of the wedge. The wedge then changes the direction of the force from a downward direction to a sideways direction. The force pushing sideways pushes the dirt out of the way so the scoop can move through the dirt. The mechanical advantage of using the wedge on the bottom of the scoop is that it changes the direction of the force you apply.

A shovel shows how two simple machines, the lever and the wedge, work together to make it easier to lift and move dirt. You gain the mechanical advantage of both simple machines. The lever and the wedge work together in a shovel to both reduce the amount of applied force needed and change the direction of the applied force. Together, this makes it easier to dig dirt than if you were just using your hands. Other complex machines work in the same way. Every complex machine has two or more simple machines working together to make getting the job they were designed for easier. By looking at what each simple machine does, you can figure out how they work together to make the complex machine work.

Stop and Think

1. Draw one complex machine you use everyday. Show the simple machines that make it up.

2. What is the mechanical advantage of each simple machine that makes up the complex machine in your drawing?

3. What is the mechanical advantage of the complex machine in your drawing? How do the simple machines that make it up work together?

4. How can you tell if a machine is a complex machine or not?

What's the Point?

Machines with few, if any, moving parts are called simple machines. These machines can be combined to create a complex machine. A complex machine can be a heavy-duty backhoe or hand shovel. Both of these are at least two simple machines combined into one machine. Simple machines and complex machines all have mechanical advantage. For example, when you use a shovel, you trade force for distance. Mechanical advantage makes the moving or lifting of heavy things easier.

4.3 Explore

What Simple Machines are Combined to Make Complex Machines?

You investigated how simple machines can help to move big things. You also learned that it often takes two or more simple machines, combined together into a complex machine, to get big jobs done. In the last section, you read about how simple machines can be combined to make complex machines. Now, you are going to revisit some more of the machines that you may have seen at the construction site or in the video. You will also think about some machines that you are familiar with from everyday life. Working with your group, you are going to identify the simple machines that make up each machine and describe how they work together.

Procedure

For each machine pictured at left and on the next page, answer the following questions:

1. What is the machine designed to do?

2. List all of the simple machines you see that make up the complex machine. What is the mechanical advantage of each simple machine?

3. Make a list of other simple machines that you think might make up the complex machine but you cannot see in the picture. Describe what you think each of them might do and what you think their mechanical advantage is.

4. What is the mechanical advantage of the complex machine?

5. What is the name of the machine?

Project-Based Inquiry Science

Reflect

Think of a task that you do everyday. It may be washing the dishes, cleaning your room, or carrying your backpack. Design a complex machine, made up of at least two simple machines that could help you do the job more easily. Make a drawing of your machine and name it. Write a brief description of each simple machine in your complex machine. What is the mechanical advantage of each? Explain what the mechanical advantage of your complex machine is and how it makes getting the job done easier for you.

What's the Point?

It is important to carefully observe combinations of simple machines. When you observe a machine's parts and watch how it works you can find the simple machines in the complex machine. By looking at each part of the machine, it is easier to figure out how the machine actually helps do work. Then it is possible for mechanical advantage to be determined. Mechanical advantage, the trade-off of force for distance, is different for all machines and makes it easier to move large, heavy objects.

More to Learn

Energy and Energy Transformations

mechanical energy: the energy an object gets when work is done on it.

energy: the ability to make something move.

potential energy: the energy an object has as a result of its position.

kinetic energy: the energy of motion.

transformed: changed from one form to another.

The biologists will be doing work to lift the crate from the beach to the top of the cliff. They have to apply a force on the crate to move it over a distance. When you apply a force over a distance, you do work. As the biologists do work on the crate, the energy of the crate changes. When work is done on an object it gets energy. This type of energy is called **mechanical energy**. What is energy? **Energy** is the ability to make something move.

When the crate is sitting on the beach, the biologists have to use their energy to move it. As they lift the crate above the beach, the biologist's energy becomes the **potential energy** of the crate. Potential energy is energy because of position. As the crate is moving toward the top of the cliff, the potential energy continues to increase. Once the crate is at the top of the cliff, the energy of the crate is potential energy. The crate has the potential to do work, to move, by falling.

If the crate fell from the cliff, the potential energy of the crate would change into **kinetic energy**. As the crate falls to the beach, the potential energy becomes less because the position of the crate is lower. At the same time that the potential energy is becoming less, the kinetic energy of the crate is becoming greater. The potential energy is changed to kinetic energy. As the crate falls toward the beach, the potential energy is **transformed** into kinetic energy.

When the falling crate hits the beach, the energy of the crate will be transformed again. When the crate breaks, some of the energy will be transferred into the pieces flying away from the crate. Some of the energy will be transformed into the sound of the crate hitting the beach.

Energy is not created, or destroyed, but changes from one type of energy to another. In this example, energy started as the biologists' energy as they lifted the crate. Then the energy became potential energy as the crate moved to the top of the cliff. As the crate fell, the potential energy was transformed into kinetic energy.

Answer the Big Question

How Do Machines Help Move Large, Heavy Objects?

The Big Challenge

Recall your challenge for this Unit. Three biologists, Drs. Enrique Cortez, Susan Diamond, and Tanika Patankar are planning a yearlong trip to an island in the middle of an ocean. They will need to have supplies delivered to them once a month. The best delivery method is for the supply crate to be dropped to the beach from an airplane.

The supply crate will be on the beach, but their campsite is on top of a nearby cliff. They must be able to get the crate from the beach to the top of the cliff. They have some 100-m lengths of very weak rope. You modeled this situation using a single strand of cotton thread, a weight, and a box with a ring stand. The weight is a scaled-down model of the crate. The box and ring stand represent the cliff. The results showed that the single thread, representing the weak rope, was not strong enough to lift the weight. Therefore, a machine will be needed to get the job done.

The biologists will not have any equipment or motorized machines. They will only be able to bring a few tools with them. Your challenge has been to think of a machine that they can build to lift the crate. You are to design and build a scaled-down model of the machine that will achieve the challenge.

Criteria and Constraints

Before you get started, make sure you understand what your challenge is. Restate it in your own words. As a class, specify the criteria and constraints. Remember that criteria are conditions that must be satisfied to achieve the challenge. In other words, you need to specify the job the machine must do. Constraints are factors that limit how you can solve a problem. For this challenge, one of the constraints is that you can only use a limited set of materials.

Plan Your Design

Draw a picture of your proposed design. Be sure to identify the following:

- the type of simple machines to be used

- the location of the applied force for each machine

- the location of the weight to be lifted for each machine

- the location of the cotton thread that will be used for each machine

- a description of the mechanical advantage of each machine (the force-distance trade-off)

- the mechanical advantage of the complex machine if you are using more than one

If you are combining more than one simple machine into a complex machine, show how the two simple machines will be connected to work together. List the materials you will need to build your machine.

Communicate

Plan Briefing

When you are planning a design, the opinions of others can be very helpful. They can help you figure out how well your design meets the criteria of the challenge. In a *Plan Briefing*, you present your design plan. You must present it well enough so that your classmates can understand your ideas. They should be able to let you know if you have made any mistakes in your reasoning. Then they can provide you with advice before you begin building your machine. As a presenter, you will learn the most from a *Plan Briefing* if you can be very specific about your design plans and about why you made your design decisions. You'll probably want to draw pictures, maybe providing several views. You certainly want everyone to know why you expect your design to achieve the challenge.

Groups will take turns making presentations. After each presentation, the presenting group will take comments and answer questions from the class. When presenting, be very specific about your design plan and what evidence helped you make your design decisions. Your presentation should answer the following questions:

- What are the features of the design?

- For each, what criterion will it achieve? Why is this the right way to achieve that criterion?

- Are there any problems you foresee with this design?

- What do you predict will happen when you use your machine to lift the weight?

- Is there anything you need help with?

As a listener, you will provide the best help if you ask probing questions about the things you don't understand. Be polite when you point out errors and misconceptions in the reasoning of others. These kinds of conversations will allow listeners to learn as well. For each presentation, if you do not think you understand the answers to the questions above, make sure to question your classmates. When you ask them to clarify what they are telling you, you can learn more. They can learn too, by trying to be more precise.

Revise Your Design

Iteration is a process of making something better over time. Designers iteratively make designs better over time. Each time they test a design, they might find ways to improve it. Recall that each change and new design is called an iteration.

You may have thought that you could easily design and build a machine to lift a heavy weight using just a string. You have even done investigations that would help you with your final design. However, you can begin to see that your early designs need to be improved. Improving upon your first design is important. That does not mean that early designs are not important. They help you to build a better machine.

Use the notes from your *Plan Briefing* to revise your machine so that it is ready to build. Draw a picture of your revised design. Be sure to identify the type of simple machine to be used. If you are combining more than one simple machine into a complex machine, show how the two simple machines will be connected to work together. Also indicate the location of the applied force, the weight, and strand of thread. Describe the mechanical advantage of the machine (the force-distance trade-off).

Be sure to add any new materials you will need in addition to your first equipment list.

Build and Test Your Design

You will now build and test your machine for the design challenge. Before testing the machine with the single strand of cotton thread, you will measure the force and distance needed to lift the object with and without the machine. From this data, you will be able to describe the mechanical advantage of your machine. After testing your machine with the thread, you will record the results, describe the strengths and weaknesses of your design, and share your designs and results with the class. From class discussions, you will be able to make recommendations for how to improve your design. You will be given an opportunity to modify your design and test it one last time.

Testing Your Design

How will you test your machine? Describe what you will measure. (Remember, you need to describe the mechanical advantage of your machine). It is important to gather accurate data. That will require several trials. Be sure to use the same procedure with each trial.

Recording Your Work

As you test and revise your design, it will be important to record the results of your tests. You will also need to record the changes you are making. You should record why you are making those changes. This is for several reasons:

- Sometimes, what seems like a mistaken approach turns out to work better when some other part of the design is changed.

- You may need to remember what you did and did not test.

- You can use your earlier designs to help teach others.

- Study your earlier designs. You can learn how your mistakes and successes contributed to your science understanding.

As you record what you are doing, you can save time by copying the parts of your design that work well. You do not have to rewrite them each time. Use *Testing My Design* pages to record your results, changes and reasons for your changes. Make sure your reasons are supported by evidence. Use one page for each iteration of your machine.

Testing My Design

Name:_____ Date:_____

Each time you build and test a design idea or model, you need to test it in a fair way and record the results of that test. Use this sheet to help record your various design ideas and the result of each design.

Draw a simple sketch of your design idea or model. The sketch should help others clearly understand what the design /model looks like.	What is the key idea you were testing in this design or model?
	What did you learn from this model? Explain how effective this design or model is at accomplishing the challenge or solving the problem.
What happened when you tested the design or model?	What change do you want to test next?

Communicate

Solution Briefing

Your teacher will have you present your design-in-progress to the class in a short *Solution Briefing*. Recall that a *Solution Briefing* is very much like a *Plan Briefing*. However, it is important for it to move faster and have more focus. Be prepared to briefly present your progress. Show the design you are currently working on. Describe how it is different from what you thought you were going to build. Explain why you changed your plan. Tell your classmates what you are having trouble with and ask them for advice. Your group's experiences may provide valuable lessons for others. If you are having trouble, a *Solution Briefing* will give you a chance to get help.

Remember, you can learn a lot from attempts that did not work as well as you expected. Do not be shy about presenting what has not worked as well as you expected. You and others can learn from mistakes. Your peers can give you advice about design, construction, and testing.

Build and Test Your Final Design

It is time to finalize your machine design. Use the results of your first iteration and what you learned during the *Solution Briefing* to improve your design. Your teacher will tell you how much time you have. You may have time for several more iterations, or there may be time only for one last version of your machine. Do the best you can in the time you have available. Remember to use a new *Testing My Design* page for each new iteration. You will be presenting your final design and your results to the class and showing them how well it works.

Communicate

Solution Showcase

You will present your final design in a *Solution Showcase*. As in a *Solution Briefing*, you will present your design to the class. Because this is your final product, you will not be asking for help. Instead, you will be providing a summary of your solution and how you got to this solution. You will also explain why you think this is a good solution to the challenge. Use the science you've learned to explain why you designed your machine the way you did. This will help you better understand the science. Listening to the reasoning others did while designing will provide you with chances to see different ways machines can trade distance and force to make work easier.

So that you will be able to make an interesting and informative presentation, you will make a poster or PowerPoint® slides that showcase your solution and why you designed it the way you did. As you prepare your poster or slides and get ready for your presentation, use the following guidelines to help you:

- State the names of the group members.

- Briefly describe the challenge. (There may be visitors in the class who are not familiar with the task.)

- Include a picture of your final machine design that shows
    - the kind(s) of simple machine(s) being used
    - the location of the applied force
    - the location of the weight being lifted
    - the location of the cotton thread being used to lift the weight
    - a name for your machine

- Describe the mechanical advantage of each simple machine you used.

- If you built a complex machine, be sure to explain how the simple machines work together. What are the trade-offs for your machine?

- Describe how the object is being moved in terms of balanced and unbalanced forces.

- Describe the results of your machine. Were you able to lift the "crate" to the top of the cliff? Were you able to do it with one "rope"?

- How difficult was it to get your machine to work correctly?

- How important are the iterations you made in this investigation?

After making your presentation, you will demonstrate your machine and show the class how it works.

As you listen to the presentations of others, make sure you understand how their machines work and why they designed their machines the way they did. Be sure to ask questions if you don't understand or if you think their explanations of the science are not complete.

Reflect

- Select one good idea from another machine group's design. What are the advantages of the other design? What is the difference between how that group created mechanical advantage and how you created mechanical advantage?

- Your machine was designed to help the biologists Drs. Enrique, Susan, and Tanika to lift their supply crate to the top of a cliff. In what other situations might your machine be useful?

- Answer the *Big Question* of the Unit: *How do machines help move large, heavy objects?*. Use what you have learned in the Unit to briefly answer the question.

Update the *Project Board*

You know a lot about simple machines, complex machines, mechanical advantage, and work now. It is time to update the *Project Board* one last time. Look at the first and second columns. Are there items you thought you knew that you can now state better and put in the *What are we learning?* column? Are there questions in the *What do we need to investigate?* column that you have answers to? Put those in the *What are we learning?* column too. Make sure there is evidence in the *What is our Evidence?* column for anything you add to *What are we learning?*

You now know many different ways of achieving the challenge. Update the *What does it mean for the challenge or question?* column with what you have learned about achieving the challenge. Each way of achieving the challenge used different combinations of simple machines and created mechanical advantage in different ways. Update the *What does it mean for the challenge or question?* column of the *Project Board* with what you have learned about how simple machines can be combined with each other to create mechanical advantage and move large, heavy objects.

Glossary

balanced forces
forces that are equal in size and opposite in direction. Balanced forces do not result in any change in motion.

complex machine
a machine that is a combination of two or more simple machines.

constraints
factors that limit how you can solve a problem.

criteria
goals that must be satisfied to be able to successfully achieve a challenge.

effort
the applied force.

energy
the ability to make something move.

first-class lever
a lever in which the fulcrum is positioned between the effort (applied force) and the load (weight being moved).

fixed pulley
a pulley in which the shaft that the wheel rotates around (axle) does not move.

free pulley
a pulley in which the shaft that the wheel rotates around (axle) does move.

friction
the force that opposes the motion of two objects that are in contact.

fulcrum
the point about which the rigid bar of a lever pivots.

gravity
the force that pulls everything towards Earth.

inclined plane
a sloping surface connecting a higher level to a lower level.

kinetic energy
the energy of motion.

lever
a simple machine made up of a rigid bar that pivots around a fixed point (called a fulcrum).

load
the weight being moved or the resisting force.

machine
a device that helps you do work more easily than without it.

mechanical advantage
the amount a machine increases the force applied to an object. As a trade-off, the distance that the object must be moved is increased.

mechanical energy
the energy an object gets when work is done on it.

model
a way of representing something in the world to learn more about it.

newton
a unit used to measure force.

pivot
the point on which something rests and turns.

potential energy
the energy an object has as a result of its position.

pulley
a simple machine made up of a wheel with a groove that holds a rope.

rigid
stiff.

second-class lever
a lever in which the load is positioned between the fulcrum and the applied force.

simple machine
a machine with few or no moving parts.

slope
the measurement of the steepness or incline.

third-class lever
a lever in which the effort is positioned between the fulcrum and the load.

trade-off
 the giving up of one thing in exchange for another.

transformed
 changed from one form to another.

unbalanced forces
 forces applied to an object in opposite directions and not equal in size. Unbalanced forces result in a change in motion.

wheel and axle
 a simple machine made up of a wheel (a circular object) that turns around an axle (a circular object that is smaller than the wheel).

work
 when a force acts on an object and the object moves a distance in the direction of the force, then work has been done.

Glosario

carga
el peso que se mueve o la fuerza resistente.

criterios
metas que se deben satisfacer para cumplir un reto con éxito.

fricción
la fuerza que se opone al movimiento de dos objetos que están en contacto.

fuerza
la fuerza empleada.

fuerzas balanceadas
las fuerzas que son iguales en tamaño y opuestas en dirección. Las fuerzas balanceadas no resultan en ningún cambio de movimiento.

fuerzas desniveladas
las fuerzas aplicadas a un objeto en dirección opuesta y de diferente tamaño. Las fuerzas desniveladas resultan en un cambio de movimiento.

fulcro
el punto de apoyo en el que la barra de la palanca gira.

gravedad
la fuerza que tiene la Tierra para atraer las cosas.

intercambio
la renuncia de una cosa a cambio de otra.

máquina
un aparato que ayuda a hacer trabajos con más facilidad que sin éste.

máquinas complejas
una máquina que es la combinación de dos o más máquinas simples.

máquina simple
una máquina que cuenta con pocas partes movibles o ninguna.

modelo
una forma de representar algo en el universo para aprender más de él.

newton
una unidad usada para medir la fuerza.

palanca
una máquina simple que consta de una barra rígida que gira alrededor de un punto fijo (llamada fulcro).

palanca de primer género
una palanca en el que el fulcro se posiciona entre la fuerza (la fuerza aplicada) y la carga (el peso que se está moviendo).

palanca de segundo género
una palanca en la que la carga se posiciona entre el fulcro y la fuerza aplicada.

palanca de tercer género
una palanca en la que la fuerza se posiciona entre el fulcro y la carga.

pendiente
la medida de algo empinado o inclinado.

pivote
el punto en que algo descansa y gira.

plano inclinado
una superficie en pendiente que conecta un nivel superior con un nivel inferior.

polea
una máquina simple que consta de una rueda con un disco que sostiene a una cuerda.

polea simple fija
una polea en la que el eje por la que gira la rueda no se mueve.

polea simple móvil
una polea en la que el eje por la que gira la rueda se mueve.

restricciones
factores que limitan cómo resolver un problema.

rígido
firme.

rueda y eje
una máquina simple que consta de una rueda (un objeto circular) que da vueltas alrededor de su eje (un objeto circular que es más pequeño que la rueda).

trabajo
cuando una fuerza actúa sobre un objeto y el objeto se mueve en una distancia en dirección de la fuerza, luego el trabajo ha terminado.

ventaja mecánica
la cantidad de fuerza que incrementa una máquina a un objeto. Como intercambio, la distancia en que el objeto se debe mover se incrementa.

Picture Credits

Photos on page 21, 57: *Jason Harris*

Photo on page 35: *Victoria Willows*

Photos on pages 3, upper, 7, upper left, upper right, 20, 38, upper left, upper right, lower, 51, 55, middle, 96: *Fotolia*

Photos on pages 3, lower, 4, 12, 16, upper, 17, lower, 27, 32, upper, 34, 39, upper, 40, upper, 45, 56, upper left, 66, upper, middle, lower, 74, 75, 78, upper, lower, 83, 86, 88, lower left, lower middle, 89, upper, 90, right, 91, upper, lower, 101, middle, lower right, 104, upper, lower, 105, upper left, upper right, lower left, lower right, 107, upper, middle, lower: *istockphoto*

Photos on pages 39, lower, 66, middle, 87, 89, lower left, 94, 101, upper, lower left, lower middle, 104, upper: *flickr*

Photo on page 54: *Big Stock Photo*

Illustrations: *Dennis Falcon*

Technical art: *Marie Killoran, Michael Hortens, Emily Yates*